# GIRLBOSS, GATEKEEP, GASLIGHT

# GIRLBOSS, GATEKEEP, GASLIGHT

### A 2020 MEMOIR

## OLIVIA STEVERMER

NEW DEGREE PRESS

GIRLBOSS, GATEKEEP, GASLIGHT
A 2020 Memoir

ISBN    978-1-63730-820-2   Paperback
        978-1-63730-882-0   Kindle Ebook
        978-1-63730-968-1   Ebook

# CONTENTS

---

# AUTHOR'S NOTE

———

I looked down to see one missed call from Mother. I paced back and forth on the crowded streets of a pseudo-suburb right outside New York City. Mother's eighteen-year-old daughter who had never gone so far as to drink a singular sip of alcohol had just driven over one thousand miles for a frat bro. When we last spoke two days prior, I was in St. Louis, which is where I was until 11:00 p.m. that night when I decided that Chad from Sigma Apple Pie was the love of my life.

I called my mother back, and as she listened to my plea from her end of the phone, she was not upset. My mother was actually quite intrigued by my convoluted and adventurous narrative. An older group of writers whom I had been working with at the time had a very similar reaction.

"This feels very current and unlike anything I've ever read," one of the writers said, after reading the account of my pilgrimage to discover the feelings of the poster child for apathy.

"I read it and instantly told my husband that I had just read the coolest thing ever, and it was written by an eighteen-year-old!" said another.

After hearing those comments and receiving their feedback, I learned people are really interested in learning about Gen Z *from* Gen Z, and there is a huge lack of generational understanding. The average age of a published book author is thirty-six years old (Keren 2016). For personal narrative and memoir, that average age is much higher, with any memoirist under forty being considered young (Miller 2017). A lot of people my age tend not to write books or memoirs, but I think it should happen more so we can have a greater understanding of youth.

Additionally, since we are currently living through a major historical period, it's important that we have records of it from a plethora of perspectives. Particularly in the realm of academia, older adults have a lot of questions about how students are being affected. There are quite a few statistics but not many narratives that provide insights on those "softer," less overt effects. As a Gen Z college student, I believe I can give a snapshot of Gen Z at large, and I hope this stirs much-needed discussion about the shifts happening amongst all generations.

Aside from just the current times and academia, there are many other unique characteristics of Gen Z. We struggle with mental health as we are the most depressed and anxious generation (Annie E. Casey 2021) yet are somehow bold enough to take down Wall Street and hack presidential rallies. We derive anxiousness from something as simple as placing a coffee order yet have enough animosity to overthrow societal elites. So while older generations tend to think we are a bunch of self-absorbed iced latte addicts with social media obsessions and no motivation to do anything, I couldn't disagree more. Especially after working on a political campaign, it's clear to me Gen Z is incredibly hardworking when it comes to things they are passionate about. Gen Z is the inevitable future, and it's important to understand how we are unique and what this means for that future.

I think there is a huge misunderstanding of how Gen Z uses social media and a stigma that social media is inherently evil. I have been forced to watch numerous videos about how using social media is consuming my personality and turning me into a dehydrated cardboard box. It sort of started out that way, back when I was posting duck face selfies in sixth grade and obsessing over my twenty-three likes, constantly refreshing the app in hopes of a new notification.

Yet as time has gone on and Gen Z has evolved, social media has become a great creative outlet. A lot of my friends with passions such as fitness, fashion, and food have accounts dedicated to their creations. They do somewhat care about their following and activity, but they are more so excited to share their passions with the world and inspire others rather than being obsessed over numbers. There are certainly enough influencers who have achieved feasible success to show social media has made pursuing creative interests much more practical.

Another great innovation of social media is it is great for meeting new people. Social media may have started off as a way to share things strictly with friends, acquaintances, and family, yet it has evolved into so much more. With large platforms wanting users to be able to grow their following, they have managed to modify their programs so platforms are now reaching broader geographical audiences. Like many other Gen Zers, I have met people from other states—both in person and virtually—through the fate of the algorithm. There's something incredibly fun and exhilarating about meeting the people behind the screen, and I don't think older generations understand that. Because I have used social media to meet people, this book will illustrate this uncharted euphoria.

There are a lot of Gen Z characteristics that go beyond statistics and can be difficult to understand. From my experience being from Gen Z and consistently interacting with other Gen Zers, I think we are spontaneous, and our train of thought can seem quite illogical. This snapshot of my life, along with a look into my thought process, can give the reader an understanding of those less concrete and scientific qualities to provide a better understanding of Gen Z.

Since this book does specifically capture 2020, people my age will enjoy reading a story that is in some ways like theirs and in other ways not. Often, I feel the portrayal of younger characters by older writers doesn't truly capture the present youth, so I hope my fellow Gen Zers can find some solace in this work by an author who truly understands them. I also think the parents of my fellow Gen Z folk will enjoy learning about the minds of their "edgy," "alt" offspring and garner a greater understanding of how they operate.

If you are interested in learning more about Gen Z, online learning, 2020, or Gen Z in 2020, this book is for you. Beyond the generational divide, there are a lot of parts to this book that everyone can relate to, especially if you love humor, adventure, and the journey that is coming of age. And at the heart of this book is love, a universal emotion—even if it's unrequited and for a frat bro.

# CHAPTER 1

# LOGICAL ANTITHESIS

———

Silos are bad.

Silos are bad because they inhibit communication, prevent innovation, and decrease efficiency.

I need more nuance.

Silo-specific branding narrows the focus of individual operations. Employees feel more responsible for their actions and work harder to achieve their individual objectives. However, this severely inhibits communication, preventing innovation and decreasing efficiency because—

Is that Brady from *Teen Beach Movie*?

I look up and see my surfer bro neighbor who might actually be Ross Lynch's long-lost monozygotic twin.

"Hey, what's up?" His chill vibe breaks the intensity of my focus.

I've been sitting in the common area of my first-year college dorm, intaking the vaporous remnants of another student's failed attempt at microwavable popcorn for the past seven hours. My face is glued to a document on my computer. It's far past the midnight hour, and when it's far past the midnight hour, my thoughts cannot coalesce into a coherent sentence—for schoolwork, at least.

"Oh, you know. . ." My thoughts trail off and I force pain-fully unnatural laughter to buy myself some time.

I'm at a loss for words, because how does one reply to "What's up?" Coming from the Midwest, "What's up?" means "Let's have a thirty-second conversation about nothing and pretend that our lives are going perfectly." Yet I've noticed that to people from the East Coast, "What's up?" means "Hey" and absolutely nothing more. He's from the West, and I don't know what the cultural norm is there. However, with his shaggy blonde hair and melanoma tan combo, there is no possibility he wants a genuine answer. My brain works worse than an expired condom until my facial spider veins erupt and turn my face stop-sign red, so I smile. That seems to be a socially acceptable response whenever this phenomenon happens, which is often—tbh.

"What's up?" I reply after too many seconds later. It's ironically hilarious that I just spent the past seven hours researching how to be an effective communicator yet still manage to be so fucking awkward.

"Going to LA."

Very on brand.

"OMG!" I use a lax word choice to make up for my red weirdness. "I was going to go there, but my trip got cancelled."

A flash of fear strikes his face before returning to a straight face. "Yeah, this COVID thing is kinda bad."

There's a pause between us. Both of us seem to have a sense of glooming uncertainty yet don't want to fuel the other's.

We make eye contact, exchange head nods, and say good-bye with our hand gestures. Surfer boy proceeds to make way to his natural marine habitat. He presses his palms on the large wooden doors of the building, generating a large gust of wind that brushes his teenage Bieber bush to the side. My eyes remain at the place he last was until his presence is a near distant memory. I look down at the screen. Thirty pages about communication, damn. It's 4:23 a.m.? I close my computer for the night.

I should probably go to bed, but I really want an iced coffee. 4:23 is close to 4:30, and last night an acquaintance named Maggie told me that she was leaving for Los Angeles around 4:30. That's close enough to 5:00, which is when most Starbuckses in the St. Louis area open, and the one on Dale Avenue, which is far superior to any other, opens at 5:00. An iced caramel cloud macchiato sounds so good right now.

There's this beautiful rental car service at my school. With a card and an app, the future is mine for the taking.

I barely even know Maggie, and I don't even have her phone number, but I'm determined to get this iced coffee at 5:00 a.m. instead of going to sleep. I sort through various school-related group chats to send her a private message.

"Hey, Maggie! When are you going to the airport?"

"I'm planning on leaving at 5:00. Why?"

"I can drive you"

"I'll be at the clocktower at 5:00 :)"

I deceive Maggie into thinking I am an early morning altruist when I am, in fact, just a glutinous beast using this as an ornate ploy for caffeinated bliss, portraying myself as a charitable saint when I am the fallen angel.

I leave the common room and the wooden chair with my warm sweat as a gift to the community. A few phone taps and footsteps later, my card presses against the window of a silver sedan, and it unlocks.

Maggie emanates gratitude so strongly that I feel it meters from the clocktower. My own desire for a macchiato earns me gratitude; good deeds are so deceiving. After I drive Maggie to the airport, I go to the Starbucks on Dale—a real Starbucks, not the pseudo-Starbucks on campus. There's a BIG difference. Real Starbuckses use espresso in their drinks, and I'm convinced the one on campus uses plain coffee, which isn't concentrated enough, and then they compensate with this watered-down sweetener that's halfway between sugar water and pure syrup. The iced caramel cloud macchiato has egg in the cloud, but I drink it even though I'm vegan.

I see the word "vegan" as more of an adjective than a noun. Labels create unnecessary moral hierarchy. A "sober pescatarian" is no greater than a "weekday vegetarian"—which are both tropes I frequently find. They beg to differ, which is why I hate labels. I will never let a label stand between me and my love of iced cloud macchiatos.

The taste of decaf isn't the same. I'm not saying it's worse, but it's not the taste that I prefer, so even though it's 5:00 a.m. and I need sleep, my macchiato is laced with caffeine.

I'm just now realizing how abysmal seven hours of researching effective communication methods was. An adventure sounds so good right now. After all, sleep is not a prerequisite to living life. A sunrise is a sunrise no matter how mentally incoherent.

There is a car available for the next few days, and if that's not a sign to have an adventure, I don't know what is.

The sun is starting to rise, which means the morning is already slipping away from me. I park the car, head back to my dorm, and begin my "shoveling clothes into my backpack" rendezvous. I do not know how to dress myself. Not now. Not ever. I mainly pack athletic clothing because there's less shame in not trying on my appearance than there is in trying and failing. I'm eighteen years old, 559 miles from parental guidance, and have three consecutive days of car access; there is unlimited freedom and endless possibilities.

I take a break from packing and open up my computer: *Places in the Midwest that are cool.*

Okay, so there's Mount Rushmore, which seems cool, but I'm convinced South Dakota is a social experiment, and even if it weren't, what else would I even do? Colored trees in Marquette, Michigan, look like they're straight from a catalog dedicated to fall. Pretty, but probably ugly in March. There are sand dunes near Traverse City, but that's eight hours away. Sand dunes are like a three-hour, forty-three-minute drive type of cool. Arkansas looks cool with its hot springs and caverns—feels unexpectedly bougie and a bit pretentious. An Arkansas cliff was featured in a Disney movie. A photo of myself smiling on the rock above miles of trees would look good on my Instagram.

This famous Arkansas location goes by Hawksbill Crag, is home to Whitaker Point, and borders the Ozark National Forest—not that I really care—but I know there is a show called *Ozark*, which I haven't seen, but the proximity must hold some significance. It's 8:53 a.m. If I left right now, I would arrive in the afternoon, which would be early enough to see the sunset, but I would have to drive during the day, and that's boring.

The Ozark National Forest means I'm probably going to need a tent, unless Henry David Thoreau bestows his wisdom upon me. The decision to only read the SparkNotes for *Walden* to get through AP English Language and Composition is currently one of regret. Over seven hundred consecutive days immersed in nature—how'd you do it, Henry? Thoreau should've made a less philosophical version of his book, sort of like a how-to guide. That would've been a bestseller—I just know it.

Maybe I should sleep.

I could sleep in the car throughout my voyage, but that isn't as much of a flex. Friends, acquaintances, and strangers far in the future will be far more astonished by the courageous tale of a teenage girl sacrificing her life to live amid the Arkansas wild than a tale of a bored teen chilling in a car for a few days—that's my interpretation, at least. I don't want to be at a rich friend's prestigious dinner party in five years—the type where we'd be eating homemade spicy rigatoni with imported sauce—where the founder of a tech start-up would approach me, and we'd chat about our wildest adventures as a twenty-three-year-old and middle-aged man often do. The conversation would go well until I would have to reveal my own cowardice from this very moment. The stakes are high.

My adventurous spirit brings me back to the sedan, this time throwing my backpack of random clothing into the passenger seat, and to the tent section at a department store, which is really just shelves and shelves of overpriced tarp with matching sticks. The tent market forces said, "Fuck you. Plastic is fifty dollars."

I walk to the grocery section to clear my mind for a bit. The store is neither crowded nor empty, yet the food supply is oddly low—like a fifty-fifty ratio of empty shelves to semi-filled. Next to the grocery section is the household essentials, so I have to see if the toilet paper memes are true, and they are. Shelves and shelves upholding the weight of nothing but air.

My mind is now clear. Refusing to fall victim to inelasticity combined with good marketing, I decide to buy a seven-dollar coffee instead. This tent setback is probably another sign from the universe, and the cost of this espresso alternative is at least forty-three dollars cheaper, making my decision a pure net gain. One could argue that while the twenty-four ounces are gone in under seventeen seconds, the tent is still a tangible entity, but I am happier than I was, and happiness is priceless. Macchiatos are the move.

Maybe I should sleep.

Caffeine doesn't really affect me. Yes, it catalyzes my visible anxiousness and bouncy-ball thoughts, but I can drink a coffee before bed and sleep, no problem. It's kind of a flex, so I would personally like to thank the residential life staff for placing me in a dorm that is a forty-five-second walk from the campus coffee shop. I could not have achieved my impressive tolerance without you.

I open my phone to a cringey texting app that I shall not name because I have some self-worth and refuse to be associated with using this particular application as a means of shooting my shot.

There's this guy whom I've been consistently talking to for a year yet have never met nor ever seen in-person. We are advancing in two completely separate Midwestern worlds, different states yet close enough that collision is plausible.

"Dichotomy"

I address him by his name, but for the sake of respecting his identity, he shall be referred to as what he is, which is a dichotomy—multiple distinct identities mashed into one person.

"Are you free this weekend?"

Seconds after sending the message I get a notification that the Dichotomy "is typing. . ."

"Yes, why? Are you thinking about coming to visit?"

He seems much more enthusiastic about my potential visit than I assumed he would be.

"Well, should I?"

"Yeah, that'd be so fun! Come to Geneva"

Through the blatant symbolism via the high price points of outdoor plastic, the universe has clearly warned me against camping, so I decide to ditch Arkansas entirely. The vibes the Dichotomy is sending through his messages feel like a green light. I'm a little disappointed though, because I thought he was from actual Chicago, but he's actually from a suburb. Going extremely out of my way to go to an Illinois suburb is certainly out of pocket; it might make for a nice anecdote. Actual Chicago also seems a bit hectic. Close human proximity and rising COVID-19 cases make suburbia more appealing.

Geneva, Illinois, is about an hour west of the city. It's the type of place where people hold mass amounts of pride for living in Illinois because they get clout from telling everyone they're from Chicago, even though they are from a moderately industrialized cornfield. The Dichotomy is one of those pride holders. Of all the ways I could inflict an emotional response out of him, none compare to the emotional reaction I would get from insulting his state.

Seeing people from my high school drive tractors to school singlehandedly made me a city girl. Yet here I am with my strongly negative opinions, going to the type of rural place I swore I'd never return. My foot is on the gas and my third macchiato of the day is condensing in my hand. I'm omw to an Illinois suburb near Geneva, or more specifically, a sixteen-dollar rental room in the even more rural suburb of Bolingbrook, Illinois.

I'm oddly calmed since I have a plan for the night. I'm excited to meet the guy I've only known behind the screen of my smartphone for what feels like a forever friendship. Now all that stands between me and him meeting IRL is the drive.

# CHAPTER 2

# FATE?

———

The Dichotomy entered my existence when I was seventeen and living through a naive, all-consuming high school romance—the type in every single coming-of-age movie to ever exist—two inseparable teens with no real concept of reality. My boyfriend told his parents that robotics club was running late so he could come over at 9:00 p.m. on a school night. No drugs, no sex, no alcohol—we were so mischievous, rebellious, and bad.

As a Taurus man, he always had a great appreciation for the fine subtleties. Our hangouts consisted of arguments about centrifugal force, in great debate of whether it's real or just inertia; classical economics—our discussion about the future of agricultural subsidies was one of our best; and neuroscience. We loved close dialogue and attempting to solve the world's greatest mysteries.

And on this particular night, our discussion about the basal ganglia leading into our fully-clothed kiss sesh made time fly by so fast that the message from an unknown sender, lighting up my screen at 9:49 p.m., was all the more startling.

"yooo"

We smiled, opened the message, scanned the profile, and amused by the tactics employed by a thirsty teen boy, let out a slight laugh.

"Should I reply?" I asked my boyfriend. Despite being semi-cognizant that I was in a cringey high school relationship that would ultimately fail, I wanted to be respectful, and if I were to entertain a random thirsty man as a means to humor myself, it would only be decent that I get permission first.

"Go for it."

The thought of replying still felt morally ambiguous, but I was in search of a good laugh, and we both thought this was funny. I typed the most unseasoned-baked-white-chicken-with-no-moisture-or-side-dishes type of response.

"hey"

I went back to the thirsty boy's feed. Upon second glance, I could feel the wealth, wit, major math geek, elitism, and "for the boys" energy from 391 miles away—a conglomeration of mutually exclusive identities that are somehow mashed into one person. Only in retrospect, I realize fate is more powerful than the algorithm because there is no explanation as to how we virtually collided. Despite the obvious geographical distance, our pages give off vastly different vibes. Mine screams "semi-quirky girl with a few close friends in yee yee nation" and his screams "money with an ambiguous side of intellect." His photos consist of international travel, professional sporting events, and strands of political advocacy. He didn't choose to be born into wealth or a skull with a powerhouse of a neural network, but his feed was certainly oriented around it.

The photos he was tagged in told a different story. He was always straight-faced—very standard and bland—the type of photo one would send to a casting agent who is looking for an overtly casual extra.

"what up?"

"nothing much"

He added the salt and pepper—nothing more, nothing less—to the bland, flavorless substance I gave him. I licked off the salt and pepper, put it under a hair dryer, and returned him a droughty desert.

"watching some hockey"

Ah, sports. I wouldn't have been surprised if his definition of "watching some hockey" was in person, sitting front row at United Center. I envisioned him messaging me during the breaks and dipping his overpriced stadium pretzel in gourmet cheese during the play. Whenever he got thirsty, he probably gulped down one of his seven-dollar bottled waters and lightly sipped from his father's craft beer. All of this was a bit presumptuous, but in the same way that I heavily scrutinized him, he probably did the same to me.

"ooo"

Our convo was still the Sahara, but I added a multicolored disco ball with an unsourced power outlet.

"it's pretty fun but I really don't like
the Flyers or the Penguins"

I must admit, I was thoroughly impressed by his commitment to carrying out this conversation. If someone I just started talking to sent me an "ooo" and nothing else, I would've sent them a read receipt. The fact that he kept replying when I seemed so objectively uninterested really says something. The "something" is undefined because he is a bit of a hard read despite my harsh skepticism, and there is a chance he was just incredibly desperate, but there's also a chance that an outer-worldy force was propelling the conversation with all its might. One might have called it fate.

"maybe you shouldn't be watching
hockey then"

My cold and blunt side exposed itself in the best way.

"heyyyy fuck you lol"

Alas, the conversation had been brought to life. Although the four y's made it clear he was intentional about his use of tone, and maybe even too intentional, this was the first message that felt natural. My boyfriend was still nearby, encouraging me to continue this conversation for amusement, (which I now realize was a bit inhumane and not something that I am particularly proud of), so I decided to take things to a new astral plane.

"for sure"

My intentions were dubious, and I felt more faced than a six-sided die. Despite leading on some random guy strictly for evening entertainment, I was beginning to feel heavy and the moral lines were starting to blur. There was obvious geographical distance between the Dichotomy and I, so the likelihood anything would amount to anything was obsolete.

I pulled up his page again and analyzed his photos, more specifically, his physical appearance in his photos. He had a lot of desirable features, definitely tall, and something about his presence in pictures made him seem like he had some awkward idiosyncrasies. He had this signature facial expression between a :) and a :|. It was a no-teeth smile but leaned on the side of a straight face, a socially awkward vibe that was not consistent with someone who direct messages random girls that live seven hours away.

As a chronic skeptic, I'm aware my first impression could have been wrong to some extent. Inanimate photos and delayed messages have only ever revealed about 30 percent of a person in the best case. I have taken photos of myself where I looked like an actual goddess and sent messages like I singlehandedly invented postmodernism. However, I have also completely sweat through an entire shirt in under seventy-two minutes while having the air conditioning set to sixty degrees because I was literally so nervous to be alone with a guy that I had a mild crush on. The true essence of another comes from their subtle mannerisms, and the Dichotomy seemed like the type to look at the floor while having an in-person conversation, which is by no means a bad impression, it was just the vibe.

"would you be any less confusing if
   we talked on—"

He interrupted my vibe assessment.

"no"

"am I welcome to try"

"sure"

He expanded the set of our communications by adding me on different social media, and he made sure to let me know.

"added"

"subtracted"

And I made sure to say the first thing that came to mind, which sort of became the way we communicated.

"divided"

"derivtivited"

Classic me to use terminology that could only come from places that would deem someone "smart." The strategy has worked seamlessly before, even though this attempt was an entirely made-up word. Whether it was bringing up random economic policies in casual small talk or throwing in quantum physics jargon for "out-of-pocket" jokes, I loved being seen as smart, and I typically didn't miss the mark this terribly.

"You're clearly an amazing speller"

"differentiated?"

And with that, I quickly learned that the Dichotomy does possess the extensive intellect portrayed by his feed.

"Do you like history memes?"

"yes"

We exchanged some good memes. He started it off with the Cuban Missile Crisis, to which I threw back some Andrew Jackson slander. I could feel this blossoming into a beautiful friendship faster than most.

I had always thought people who had friends online were either middle-aged men, visibly angsty teenagers, or extreme video gamers without a social life in their twenties. The Dichotomy and I, although only seventeen and arbitrary in the life beyond the teens, had impressive attributes among those our age. We were both intellectual overachievers with our own individual edges. The Dichotomy, with his notable awkwardness amplified by his unexpected extroversion and moral ambiguity, was interesting.

The Dichotomy was innately intelligent and more traditional in a sense. His mind was very much like an optimization algorithm with a heavy focus on putting in the minimal amount of effort, which was impressively minimal, to get the best recorded results in a handful of things. I focused on doing the absolute most number of things like ten activities and more coursework than the school day permitted. He had a clear division between work and play while I found ways to make my every move "productive." He was more like traditional corporate success while I was more of the entrepreneurial type.

If we were to be together in a grocery store, shopping for strawberry yogurt made from the milk of the finest cashews, The Dichotomy would likely grab the first that catches the eye because the time spent scanning the yogurts would be non-optimal for even the highest level of satisfaction that a yogurt can provide. I, however, would pick up and put down each yogurt at least ten times before making a decision because I know that finding the perfect yogurt now could reduce the time spent looking for yogurts later and potentially lead to greater satisfaction long term.

I obsess about the things that don't matter and convince myself they do. He doesn't.

"Have you taken the ACT?"

"yeah, I got a 36"

Of course, being a naive, score-obsessed teen who put way too much emphasis on the results of a three-and-a-half-hour block of time, I had to know his standardized test scores to truly assess his brilliance, and a perfect score is better than my acceptable ninety-ninth percentile, which was really on the lower end of the top 1 percent, probably only one question away from being in the top 2 percent. He was one of the few people I was incapable of flexing on.

"You will definitely get into an
elite college"

"Nooo"

Few things annoyed me more than geniuses who can't admit they are geniuses. Like it's literally so fucking cool, gloat. Flex on me. We continued talking about AP tests and scores because, being seventeen and conditioned by academic validation, we were truly convinced they mattered.

"the hockey game is over and idk
what to do now"

"learn a language or watch
a TED Talk"

"hmmm I'd rather talk to you"

"mistake"

"I'm enjoying this"

I sent a stream of random, uncorrelated icons, which is my signature response when I don't know what to say. The reaction that it prompts from the receiver tells me a lot about them. There is no standard response, or one I often see, so it's fun to see how individuality manifests itself in reaction.

"You're too smart for me to
understand what you're saying"

"derivtivited"

Ah, so he was witty, and he knew I wanted to be perceived as intelligent. He was thoughtful about his messages and used ideas that were specifically withheld in the particular conversation. He could have been charismatic, a master manipulator, or both.

We continued talking throughout the night for hours after my boyfriend left, yet before I slept, I let him know I had a boyfriend because I did have somewhat of a moral conscience—a diminishing moral conscience given that I never told my boyfriend about this late-evening texting debut, but there was still some morality there. The night of talking expanded to the week, the month, and then months. He was kind of the "guy you don't have to worry about," the close friend I interacted with that tended to emotionally cross the platonic line.

Although nothing physical or romantic could have ever really happened, there was still a forbidden energy within our friendship. I had never really been the villain or one to fall into stereotypes, but the potential for an insane chaos intrigued me. The idea that I could drive six and a half hours to cheat on my boyfriend with a genius who randomly direct messaged me while watching a hockey game consumed me with curiosity. I was captivated by the fact that this friendship had the potential for chaos, not the fact that it was unleashing chaos.

Our relationship was like the cigarette metaphor in the book by the father of crash course history videos, the ones that AP kid friend groups derive an oddly large amount of entertainment from, *The Fault in Our Stars* by John Green. My friendship with the Dichotomy was benign, but had the potential to turn into a contagious, mutated disease if given the power. It was a sharp-cutting knife in the hand of a well-trained chef. The line between innocence and guilt was cilantro leaf thin.

There was a certain chaos in the Dichotomy's mind that I see in mine. There was an absence of predictability and a logical thought train. Both of our minds were always everywhere and nowhere all at once. Neither of us knew what the other was going to do next, and certainly for me, I found that intriguing. There was a certain comfortability in being friends with someone who has a similar chaos.

Lust, on the basis of all things insubstantial, was in the air.

# CHAPTER 3

# AN INELASTIC COLLISION

———

Slightly over an hour prior, I was a young curious girl, motivated to discover the land between eastern Missouri and northeastern Chicago. Yet after passing the Arch to witness eighty miles of nothing but rest stops, gas stations, and Midwestern fast food, I've learned that some visuals are better left a mystery.

This car doesn't have an aux, and if it did, I'd probably be too indecisive to pick a song and end up driving in hours of silence, so I twist the dial to a pop station. In between the alternations of "The Box" by Roddy Ricch and "Circles" by Post Malone are ads and radio voices that appear to be in some sort of turmoil. Every song is followed by either a CDC travel advisory or an ad for a last-minute spring break getaway. Public health and unearned revenue are battling for my demise, and I would turn off the radio entirely if the two songs on rotation weren't absolute fire. Pop music has an unbearably pleasant way of etching itself into my skull.

There really isn't much to complain about because driving at night is elite. This particular landscape could certainly be more visually appealing, but the feeling of it all supersedes that. The driver's seat at night is an introspective place where creativity spurs from the blurriest, sleep-deprived thoughts. This bittersweet magic that makes you feel invincible, arbitrary, and infinite is only accessible after 10:00 p.m. on the US highway network, or so I am convinced. Driving at night just hits different, so any complaint I may have is so incredibly minute in the euphoric high of driving.

Gas station food sounds particularly good right now. Something about exploring the unique scent of dirt in rural Illinois while walking through aisles to pick out some processed, sodium-saturated carbohydrate, while being amid a melting point of people, captivates me. Gas stations are the best place to people-watch because it's one of the few universals. It's one of the few places that people go regardless of socioeconomic status, race, gender, and all else. The richest villain may be passing through on his road trip to the Hamptons while the single mother puts enough fuel in her tank to get to work. It's one of the few common places that plays with reality.

There are some archetypes that I frequently encounter. At every gas station at every night, there is always a man that makes me uncomfortable, usually middle-aged, but elderly passing. He usually looks as though he has some children, but that does not exempt him from his creepy energy by any means. He clothes himself in denim, leather, or both and drives either a motorcycle or a big truck to flaunt his macho masculinity. In addition, there is generally some type of self-classified "edgy" teen or young adult who masks themselves as being incapable of happiness; they tend to work the front counter. They're the type who could watch people steal everything in the store and continue as though nothing happened because they aren't paid enough to care. The rest of the late-night gas station crowd is variant, yet never a letdown. Whether it's a coed group of middle schoolers who emanate insecurities that are uncomfortably familiar or the chaotic family that thought a family vacation would solve all their problems, there are seldom disappointments.

When other people see me at a gas station late at night, they see the mysterious main character, a young adult with dark eye circles and a stoic presence. She wears a navy winter jacket with the hood over her hair, a singular blonde strand peaks out like she is revealing something. Her walk is so confident, yet her idiosyncrasies are so awkward. She paces back and forth with the confidence of an investment banker on Wall Street, yet her hand uncontrollably shakes as she reaches for the refrigerator door, her palm slides when she touches the handle because of her accumulation of nervous sweat, and she always ends up grabbing a random sparkling water instead of the brand she was looking for because she gets worried people are judging her.

And to their judgement, and in my defense, I argue the sparkling water I just purchased is quite good, despite not being what I was looking for. And maybe the best things are never what is intentionally sought after.

The tire treads catch the road's grooves, producing a loud rumble and shaking the car with enough force to spill my sparkling water all over my lap, which I had already finished, but in theory, the shake was definitely large enough. I am drifting—both on the road and away from my conscious thoughts. My best efforts to concentrate are by no means an effective effort, but I'm trying. My teen-age invincibility complex is a toxic illusion particularly prevalent at night.

The abundance of Culver's makes it clear it is a Midwestern staple. Thickly whisked simple carbohydrates create memories in small towns that would otherwise go unremembered. As a vegan, I cannot say I find meat slabs and frozen chicken periods particularly appetizing, but the modern vibe and stone architecture produces a youthful aesthetic, and I admire the sentiment in that. In my severely sleep-deprived state, the LED lights on the sign feel like they are welcoming me to rest in a beautiful castle home and live a warm, happy childhood I always knew existed but didn't know I could have.

The Culver's passes me by, now just an arbitrary blur in the background that's thirteen minutes away from my destination in Bolingbrook.

I hadn't really thought about the purpose of my drive until now. Like actually wtf am I doing right now? I'm eighteen. I spontaneously drove four and a half hours to Illinois to meet up with some guy that direct messaged me a year ago, a guy whom no one knows I have a connection to in a place no one knows I am in. Even I barely know where I am.

I really don't know what the purpose of this is. There are plenty of lies I could craft to justify this excursion, yet in all honestly, I don't know the real reason I'm here. Of all the things I could have done, I'm not sure why meeting the Dichotomy was the one I chose. And maybe that choice says something, but maybe it doesn't. Everything happens for a reason, but maybe not everything is really that significant. To the creators of the modern-day cereal box, the value of a cereal box is much greater than it will ever be to me.

My rental room in Bolingbrook is at the top of the steepest driveway I have ever seen, like forty-five-degree ascendent—probably. I enter and spray the bed with disinfectant because I am so woke and aware of the things happening in the world. All the viruses on the surface of the comforter have no chance to infect me—viruses 0, Olivia 1. The only plague I have to face is my internal sleep deprivation and anxiety combination. Less sleep equals more anxiety, and more anxiety equals less sleep. A swamp of gnats swarms my chest, preventing my brain from being able to power down, which is the one thing I need most. Tomorrow I will meet the Dichotomy, and that is my unavoidable destiny.

"I've arrived"

I send him a casual mirror selfie in my rental room while he's well asleep, the type of photo that looks like I didn't try, but he definitely received my eighth attempt, which was ultimately worse than the first.

It's a little past 2:00 a.m., which means I'm going to scroll through my phone for another hour and set an alarm for 8:00 a.m., so that I have no sleep in my system because I love to make myself as anxious as possible. There are only, like, one thousand cases of COVID in the United States right now, but articles and videos about Italy have found their way to my media stream. If the one thousand cases follow the same exponential growth trend as Italy, that thousand could be multiple thousands tomorrow and maybe even one million by next week. The empty toilet paper shelves are only the beginning of an impending apocalyptic doom, or maybe that's just a slippery slope, and I'm becoming a moderate conspiracy theorist. I don't want to be perpetuating a false reality so much so that I am living in a delusional state and can't discern reality from the fictional one I've crafted, but yet again what is reality, and is it really fair to say that one reality is truer than another? Yeah, that's definitely something a conspiracy theorist would say. Fuck.

The United States is okay for now, and the only thing I'll ever truly have is the present.

***

I rise to two new messages from the Dichotomy.

"I can't believe you actually came
to Illinois"

That makes two of us.

"I'm hyped"

Same.

I hold off on replying, (because don't talk to me before I've had my morning coffee *insert the cringiest strand of emoticons*).

The same chasm of "travel" and "psych don't" plays on repeat as I head to the nearest Starbucks. I can tell the spring break getaway ads were prerecorded because the tone in the radio hosts' voices for their "relatable small talk" is increasingly uncertain.

The interior of the Starbucks feels the same way. The tables are more sporadically placed than normal, and they're no longer refilling reusable cups. The people at the tables have become suspects; they could all be carriers of the biological death token.

The line to order is obsolete, which is unprecedented for Starbucks at midmorning. I've gladly waited half an hour for their coffee on multiple occasions.

"Can I get a grande iced caramel cloud macchiato made with almond milk and no caramel drizzle?"

A large group of people gather in close proximity behind me; I knew no line was too good to be true.

"Actually, can I get a venti?"

Twenty-four ounces to amplify my quirky, sporadic personality transforms me into my most typical self, which is not relaxed in the slightest and sometimes eustress but often not.

My shaky fingers enter "the bean" into my navigation software because I am unfamiliar with the area and fall victim to tourist traps as much as anyone else. Fifteen miles per hour quickly accelerates to seventy. The lanes go from two to four to six, and I am terrified. Cars cloud each of the six lanes—North, South, East, and West—and I am so small. One wrong move from any direction, and I will become a distant memory.

I arrive at a crossroad perpendicular to Jackson Boulevard, parallel to the romanticized shiny legume of interest, and I make my peaceful descent to the underground. For twelve hours of parking, $13.25 does not seem bad. I ascend to the streets by foot and explore, carrying far more than twenty-four ounces of anxiety for what I feel coming. The streets are crowded, life feels normal but also like a disillusionment. My overworn tennis shoes that are beginning to erode at the bottom take me 347 paces until I see another Starbucks. It must be my destiny to get another twenty-four-ounce iced coffee. The universe is so silly.

I'm not really sure why I came to the city. I'll be meeting the Dichotomy at some point in the next twelve hours, and I should probably reply to his text.

"Where do you want to meet?"

A straight-to-the-point message with no emotion to show that I'm not totally insane. I'm totally not alternating between my own conspiracies about the world ending while being cognizant that I could be crafting a delusion, driving around a major US city completely by myself amid it all.

"lmao, come to Geneva"

No shit.

"Like when?"

"Does 6ish work?"

"Yes, like where though?"

"I'll send you the addy"

Currently, "6ish" is a few(ish) hours away, a few(ish) hours for me to participate in hyperconsumerism. Maybe, I should get something nice for myself to wear, something nicer than my ten-dollar black knit leggings that have a hole in the crotch with my navy Minnesota state capitol sweatshirt that is about one and a half sizes too small. This could classify as a special occasion, but that could also be my own reality distortion. I could easily convince myself I am an invincible young adult, chasing greatness, and on my way to meet my forbidden lover, whom I am destined to be with forever and ever—the type that hosts dinner parties with wine and charcuterie—and only ever argues playfully about the little things.

A red long-sleeve T-shirt with some light blue mom jeans is the innovative and elite outfit I purchase from the sales rack of a department store. It's timeless styling and beautifully effortless—much unlike the photos that clusters of people, ready to rip each other's livers out, are trying to attain at the shiny legume statue. There's a certain coolness in going to a city and not doing touristy things. Instead of going to museums, I bought an outfit, which means I am basically a local.

"The addy" the Dichotomy sent me is a McDonald's parking lot—because teenage men are so good at planning hangouts.

In the parking lot that the Dichotomy sent me the address to, I see a blurry figure resembling a rotting cauliflower floret covered in dirt pacing back and forth. The off-white sweatshirt, eggshell pants, and bushy brown hair are not working in his favor, but as I've established, I can be a bit harsh, and my relationship with the Dichotomy has never been about some alluring aesthetic despite the sexual tension. It's been about discussing math in the day and receiving drunk videos of him ranting about his theories of anarchoprimitivism in the after-midnight hours. I can feel every remaining ounce of my postmodern coolness (not that it has ever been much more than an ounce) slipping away from me as my shaky, visible anxiousness increases.

The curiosity in his eyes meets the fear in mine. He does an awkward hand raise and approaches my car.

"Olive Garden?"

I smile at his impromptu nickname. Out-of-pocket nick-names with intentional irony have always been our thing, and this would have been incredibly cringey in any other context.

He sits in the passenger side. I can see him scanning me up and down through my peripherals. Neither of us truly know what the other looks like. We have decent ideas, yet only so much of a portrait can be captured at first glance.

Every word that escapes his lips is arbitrary. There's something oddly comforting about his physical presence, so much so that the context of our dialogue seems unimportant.

I don't have a strong opinion of him. Typically, when I meet people, I default to binary associations like good and bad, nice and mean, protagonist and antagonist. He, however, feels very nuanced and layered unlike most. There is a lot going on within him, and it's quite unsettling, yet I love it. I don't understand him, and I don't feel like I need to. He isn't a painting meant to scour for meaning until its color is gone. He is a sculpture meant to be incomprehensible—a displayed shape that feels like fifteen dimensions happening all at once.

We aren't in love, and we never will be. That's all I really know.

I stop the car, and he takes me down to this small city park with a nice little river, cemented pathways, and the type of ominous orange streetlights that would flicker as a sign of danger in a horror film. The air smells of wet dirt from piles of snow that had recently melted. Our bodies occasionally collide as we walk along the narrow path like we are drawn to each other by forces we can't explain.

"Give me a year," he says randomly.

"What?"

"Don't ask, just give me a year."

"Okay, 1978."

"Jimmy Carter,"

"Okay?"

"That's who was president in 1978."

My speechlessness signals him to go on.

"You know. Camp David Accords. Airplane deregulation. Humphrey-Hawkins employment bill."

He says this as though it was common knowledge that I should have at the top of my head, the same way someone would expect me to know that Thursday comes after Wednesday. Needless to say, he's even smarter than I thought he was. We continue our little game, and I'm slightly afraid that if he gets too close to the river he might malfunction because he's actually a supercomputer with a thin layer of human flesh coating the exterior.

The lights around us slowly dim out until the only light left is the artificial orange. We know it's time to depart. With about of foot of space between us, we turn towards each other for a quick embrace. A short pause. A longer embrace.

"It's good to know you actually exist," he says.

I'll see him again. I just know he will be a stable constant in my life of chaotic variables.

I bring him back to the place we first met. Uncertainty is in the air, yet I feel more at peace with my incomprehension. I head back to my room in Bolingbrook.

I look at myself in the mirror, wearing the red long-sleeve shirt with light blue mom jeans, the ones I bought earlier today, and let out a slight laugh. The figure in front of me is so young, so far from where she will be—for better or worse.

Time will go on.

# CHAPTER 4

# GOODBYE WORLD

———

I wake up and grab my phone from the wooden nightstand beside my bed. The screen stays black for quite some time to alert me that my phone is void of notifications, so I scroll through social media as my addicted self does. The first post on my feed is by this guy who lives on my floor. He's wearing a large smile and light blue swim trunks. Sand holds onto his calves, droplets of the Atlantic cling to his upper body. He's at Miami beach with four other friends, and they seem to be having a great time. People's posting doesn't reflect the news, which is calming. It's still selfies, beaches, and spring break. Maybe I worry too much. I mean I already know I worry way too much, but maybe my intuition is off just this once.

My visit with the Dichotomy feels painfully incomplete as if it's foreshadowing for something greater to come. We came together like concrete and parted at the speed of wind.

I'm still in Illinois, which I can't say is particularly beautiful or a great spring break getaway, but it's something new. I should enjoy it while it lasts. I put my phone away and head back to the city. There are, yet again, cars all around me. The freeway is crowded, yet fast. The high volume of traffic is my sign the world is continuing.

I can't turn the radio on. I don't want to be afraid. I want to hear nothing but the noises from the masses of people to know that there is order in this world. Chicago is the third-largest city in the United States. It's loud, there's traffic, and I want to hear it.

I drive faster and faster to distract myself from my thoughts. Life will go on. Everything will be fine. The faster I drive, the more I put myself in danger. The severity of the danger makes me focus on driving and nothing else. If I think about anything else, I could die, so I must use all mental capacity to stay alert.

When I was fifteen with my learner's permit, my mother figured the best driving practice would be driving us from Minneapolis to Chicago, (i.e., I convinced my mother we should go to Chicago and used mandatory driving hours as the primary reason). It was one of my first times behind the wheel, and I couldn't even distinguish the turn signals from the windshield wipers. I left our home at a slow and steady fifteen-mile-per-hour pace. The speed soon became thirty, then sixty, and I could handle it with guidance. Although I was repeatedly scolded for almost drifting into the ditch, it was fine. Yet when the six-and-a-half-hour drive brought us into the night, and time had gotten away from us, we began to relax at the worst time. Suddenly, there were cars all around, seven lanes of traffic, and a driver with no experience behind the wheel.

Years later I channel that same energy. I need to be alert and aware, yet in a way that does not revolve around my fears of the world. So I drive faster and faster until I find somewhere to park.

I think driving is one of the only times anyone can truly be mindful. There are so many distractions that it takes the consequence of distraction being *death* to fully focus. From being distracted by calculus memes to mediocre men with the personality of chalk contacting me in attempt to fuck, I'm never truly in the moment.

I don't really know how to park. When I took my driver's test, I failed every type of park that could be failed, yet somehow managed to pass. I pull into a parking garage and jerk my head to grab an entry ticket, casting my vision away from the rates. If I know how much this parking garage is going to cost, I won't have a good time because I'll just be thinking about how much I was robbed.

I make it to the third level. There's an open view of brick buildings and a neon sign advertising Chicago-style pizza. I pull out my phone again, but this time I can't avoid my headspace. I have over one hundred new notifications from group chats and emails, and I can't escape it. I'm in a parking garage, and there's nothing I can do to distract myself.

*"There will be no in-person courses taught in the classroom or any other setting . . . you are not permitted to return."*

And now I really can't avoid it. Despite the comforting permeance of the brick in the buildings, the world has been crumbling and now it is collapsing. I knew it.

I need to drive again. The parking garage—almost literally, but still figuratively—puts its hands around my neck and strangles me against a concrete wall until I cough up seventeen dollars for my five-minute stay.

I continue to be suffocated after my departure; there are cars all around me. I cannot go fast enough to avoid my thoughts. I sit beside them in the passenger seat. My thoughts are the driver, and I never feel as though I am entirely in control. I can guide but not control them.

My thoughts are taking me to where I should've been. I was supposed to be in Los Angeles with Mother. My thoughts extend their hand to the radio dial and play "L.A. Story" by Sammy Adams to remind me of how many times I listened to that song amid long, hopeless nights in the library, wishing something good could come.

My academic life is in shambles. Not because I don't care, but maybe because I care too much. I envision an image of my dorm room, which feels foreign to me. The library feels much more like home. I think back to when a 33 percent on my first college exam revealed itself in the middle of my computer screen. The people whom I had been studying with on the top floor of the library, which was by far the quietest and most practical for studying, had much more fortunate percentages in the middle of their screens. I laughed it off. There are rows and rows of poorly stained wooden bookshelves filled with literature that no one will ever read—stories and lifetimes that will never be known.

Sometimes I would study by myself: a workstation severed away from others yet close enough to the entrance in hopes that someone magnificent will walk through the door and change my life as I sit and work for hours and hours. Knowledge increases alongside fear of failure. My chest tightens when I close my eyes at night, reminding me I can do more. I can work harder.

I think of Los Angeles. The tears from my cheeks amid a mental breakdown in the library bathroom will make their debut into the Pacific. Palm trees and disingenuous smiles that feel real remind me nothing actually matters. My high school physics teacher turns on the projector. "We're going to be watching a film about heat death." Shapes come and go. They multiply and become more convoluted with time.

Disorder is a strictly increasing property. The disorder in the world is incapable of becoming more orderly. Life will only get more chaotic.

If it feels like my world is ending now, then tomorrow can only be worse because the world is ending because of chaos, and chaos can only increase. I have to do everything I can to maximize my time before the people around me catch up to my level of disorder. Life is happening right now, and I should enjoy it, but I want to drive really fast because driving really fast and far makes me feel really productive and it's not something I'm afraid of failing at. When I make it super far, I feel good and happy and like I accomplished great things, and I want to feel good and happy, and I am otherwise incapable of anything, so I must go now, but the traffic is so bad that I am stuck, and I want to cry, but I am so numb from the academic pressure I constantly put on myself that I can't release my own emotions. All the energy from a flood stream of tears is trapped inside me and there's nothing I can do but sit here and take it.

I push my thoughts out of the car and into the Chicago traffic. They need to get run over again and again for the time being. Foot on the gas till I'm back to my dorm building. No thoughts. Head empty. Just logistics.

\*\*\*

At 7:00 a.m. the next day, the voices of middle-aged masculinity wake me. Two deep and raspy voices are closer than I am comfortable with and discussing matters I cannot discern. They seem even closer to me than the hallway. A loud bang comparable to an anvil being dropped thunders from the room next to me. There are people in my suite.

Outside my door there are large boxes and tape and devices with wheels used to transport things. My suitemate must have hired movers to get her stuff. I put some decent clothes on and make my descent to the rest of the building. I roam the halls to see the number of closed doors equivalent to the number of open; one to one closed to open doors is an unprecedented ratio. There are parents with their children rushing to get their belongings as if they knew something striking about the imminent future.

Bottles of alcohol fill the recycling, trash, and compost bins to signify the pure panic of college students rushing to hide their alternate personas from their parents. The tension in the long car rides home will be stronger than the smell of spilled alcohol in a tight, suffocating trash room. The elephant always feels much larger in a small car.

I'm an athlete. No one ever expects it, but it's the truth. I don't watch sports or understand how they work, and I genuinely couldn't tell you a football position other than quarterback, but I am an athlete. I do track, except I'm a thrower, and I like when people guess my event because no one can ever figure it out, so it makes me feel extra quirky.

There's a lot of commotion throughout the track group chat. Teammates are rushing back to say their goodbyes. Forsyth Boulevard is turning into party city as a prelude to the isolating underworld.

The CDC recommends avoiding large gatherings, but no one seems to care. A flock of people wait for me at the clocktower to join the hundred others ready to forget that the world is ending at the infamous track house. I know their names, faces, life history even, but I don't know them behind the facts.

There's this one sparkly blue sweater in my closet that makes its way to every social outing I attend. It's kind of ugly, but I love it. It's so thin that it's almost unintentionally sheer with long sleeves and tight cuffs that strangle the wrist, creating this voluminous sleeve. The body of the sweater clings to my stomach like a Gravitron, and it's most definitely my favorite.

My sparkly blue sweater and I fade into the background of this party scene, taking it in as an outside observer. The track house is nice. A hand-drawn chalk image of a curly-haired women is etched into the walls. Tape outlines of different team members' heads and faces occupy the living room. I can only imagine the backstories behind the images and how much it must hurt to spontaneously lose touch with the people in the walls.

And that's probably why everyone around me is crying. I have a Capricorn moon, which means I don't feel emotions often and definitely not publicly. I do not feel sad. I am the tape on the wall, but just the tape, not the face.

I feel like I'm at a funeral with a playlist made for a middle school dance. It's the death of youth hosted by Mr. Worldwide.

The life behind the voices continues throughout the night. I leave on my own accord around 3:00 a.m., walking alone, back to my dorm, and into the empty streets. The terrors of the night are hiding from me. It seems even they are scared of social crowding.

# CHAPTER 5

# MYSELF AND MY THOUGHTS

———

The location I returned to stayed with me through the coming weeks, and there's nowhere I'd rather spend my surprise second week of spring break than in my first-year college dorm. You may be confused by the logistics behind this circumstance, but I assure you they're unimportant.

An economist once told me being alone is the detriment of happiness. That statement has sat with me for quite some time. By that logic, success and happiness are almost entirely mutually exclusive ideas, which seems more plausible than I would like it to be.

Being alone is an adventure, an explorative state. Being alone is the only time that one can truly preserve their authenticity. When alone, the world is a product of your perception. 3:33 is no longer the time of day; it is a sign of your thriving imagination.

Being alone is a constant reminder I can always start over, and no one has to know. I don't have to say goodbyes and give explanations, I can just move to Los Angeles and throw my elite degree in the trash to become an actress.

I've actually always wanted to be an actress. When I was eight, I was accepted into a top acting agency in my home state of Minnesota, which isn't a particularly fantastic state for acting, but it could've been worse, like Arkansas or something. Anyway, it was about an hour from my home, and my math ability was too good to squander, so it was decided that I would decline the offer. Since then, I've always found it hard to get back into acting. It continues to live at the back of my mind, but I'm at a top-twenty university now, and it would be silly to let my brain go to waste.

My dorm is plain as all can be. A teenage boy can decorate better than I can. The walls are a dark vanilla, and the floor is a patterned gray. There is a wooden desk, a wooden dresser, and a wooden bed frame with a mattress. There are actually some posters beneath the bed. One with a cringey science quote layered on top of a picture of Albert Einstein. One with Mike Tyson. One with Eleven from *Stranger Things.*

I think it would've been funny to get a poster of some random guy my age that got famous online just for being "hot." A guy who has incredibly questionable ethics, comes across as a tool because he probably is, and would've been canceled at least seven times if he was a gender other than a man.

There is a family living in a room down the hall, a husband and wife with two prodigy children. I don't know much about the wife except she has a blog where she documents her battle between living in a dorm and the wrath of parent Karens. Her husband is a Yale alumnus. Before the isolated times, the children would occasionally do their homework at the common room table. They were always so full of vocabulary words. Andragogy, acquiesce, hiraeth—to name a few. They are very intellectually advanced; it feels weird to refer to them as children.

They're always playing music, quite loudly and inconsistently paced. It's always one instrument at a time, but never the same instrument two days in a row. I didn't realize they were making the sound behind the music until they left their door open slightly enough that light could reflect a large brass instrument.

They're a family of geniuses, and they are very nice people, but we keep to ourselves.

There are a few other students in the buildings, with names I care to know but likely never will. Maybe, I'm not the only who likes to be alone. The word got out about how amazing solitude can be.

I enjoy walking down the dorm halls. The doors are still decorated with names and fun additions that make me wonder about the people who lived there. I often find myself walking past the door of my first ever friend with benefits, or FWB as a cool and #relatable person might say. Of course, I only know it was a friend with benefits in retrospect. At the time, I thought he was my soulmate because soulmates come over after 10:00 p.m. and ask you questions like "Why would we talk about our lives when we can make out instead?"

It was only a couple months ago, but I was years younger. I didn't know that the college man's greatest fear was commitment.

Nothing is more intimate than when it's late and the consciousness is shut off, leaving the words up to the great subconscious who is unaware of the doubts and fears that filtered words hold, and you're with someone, a person of interest. Your bodies are close to each other, and you feel the presence of the other person that others seldom get the chance to feel. You hear their real passions that they publicly hide with their postmodern apathy and crafted elevator pitch comprised of nothing but socially conditioned lies, so you share yours too. You form a bond that extends itself to another astral plane; it's beyond comprehension of your whole physical realm. It feels like love even if it isn't, and when you're a first-year in college, it definitely isn't, but you don't know that yet, which is why the first consistent interaction is a game changer.

At the end of the day, you are the only person you'll truly ever have. Your grip around their shoulder as you lie late at night will never be tight enough to make them stay. I told *him* that I wanted to be an actress, which was relieving. I never tell anyone that I want to be an actress.

It hurt to learn our interactions were my imagination's finest creation, but that's the way it goes. Relationships aren't as deep as I have a tendency to make them. Nothing is as deep as I tend to make it. In a world of increasing distractions, depth is a kiddie pool.

The dining halls have been open with a variety of chefs staffed and ready, but there's something so appealing about sugar cereal and smoothies. I politely reject specially pre-pared food and the prodigy family's continuous offering to get groceries for me.

I have absolutely zero motivation for school once this second spring break ends, and I'm definitely not alone in that. Group chats and messages from friends are filled with dialogue about purposelessness. College feels like no more than a letter on a page, and maybe that's all it ever was. A letter on a page with a knife to my throat and a hand around my lungs that squeezed tighter as I worked harder. Just a letter.

Showing up to high school decked out in my college's branded merch was my only sense of style after receiving a congratulatory letter of acceptance from a top-twenty school. Conversations with friends became a challenge to insert elitism as much as I possibly could while still portraying psuedo-humility. The pointlessness of college and the arrogance I have about going somewhere prestigious cannot coincide, which is most definitely for the better.

There isn't much to do. I don't like movies or TV shows because I do not like to process new information that will not make me more productive in some way. Maybe that's a flaw, but society would never let me admit that. The inability to relax could never be seen as a problem in a system that thrives off the optimization of human output.

There are no tears even though it feels like there should be. There is nothing to talk about and nothing to feel.

The only thing that makes me feel is checking the COVID tracker. The graph of cases forms a parabola, and we are so fucked, and every day we grow increasingly fucked. My chest tightens and my heart races, but at least anxiety is something to feel.

Sometimes I analyze the trends and try to make my own predictions. It makes me feel like I have control in the world when I obviously don't, and people like to hear my insights in a time when nothing feels certain.

My current prediction is this will last until at least the end of the year, November to be precise. Based on Italy's numbers scaled to match the United States, this seems like it'll be around for much longer than the April 15 prediction.

A few days prior, I used a dating app to find the most generic man I possibly could. He had the personality of sheetrock and couldn't hold a conversation to save his life. When he asked me if I wanted to hang out, I said yes. He came over, kissed me, and two minutes into the make out sesh, he left to go hit his vape. I didn't let him back in, but it was a nice distraction at the time. There's comfort in knowing that even when it feels like the world is ending, some things, such as classic fuckboy-ery, will remain.

I'm still lying on my back on my bed with my thoughts next to glass jars of dirt. At the start of the semester, I attempted to grow corn stalks because I thought it would be really funny if stalks of corn grew in my room. It didn't work and now I'm left with dirt.

The bottles of alcohol in the trash room are starting to sound more appealing. A half-empty bottle of Malibu rests at the top of a recycling bin, on the verge of falling to the floor as though it's meant for someone to take it and guzzle it down at the start of the night. That someone could never be me though. You can take a college kid to parties, but you can't make it drink.

Every day for the next day until October is probably going to be like this. Day in and day out of white walls, gray carpet, and processed foods—so boring that endless lines at the DMV start to sound appealing.

I need something to keep my life interesting. Something to work toward. Something challenging with a moderately high failure rate and a failure that would be a funny story and maybe even a little cringey. Definitely something I can't tell without blushing. The type of story I would only tell an acquaintance whom I was certain I would never see again in fear that it might resurface. An unattainable pursuit of some sort, but not so unattainable that it's predictable.

The dirt in the jars immersed from irony, a thought of how funny it would be to bring something so unfitting and unsettling into my existence. A corn stalk isn't meant for a dorm room, much less a glass jar. With the perfect amount of sunlight, soil, and water, it is possible. Not right and still quite wrong, but possible, ironic, and not meant to be.

My only escape from this monotony is the pursuit of Chad from Sigma Apple Pie.

## CHAPTER 6

# CHAD FROM SIGMA APPLE PIE

—

Even if I didn't search the internet to uncover his past, immediately after the first time I saw his perfect face, figure, and unexpected niceness, I would know he was a former lacrosse player. He's six foot, four inches with brown hair, brown eyes, and perfectly shaped eyebrows. He's, in my most colloquial language, chill and objectively attractive. I don't think he can see further than five seconds into the future, but I feel that way about almost every guy I meet.

He's too attractive to take me seriously. I'm the type of girl he'd keep around to send him homework answers or give him head on a random Tuesday. He knows he is insurmountably attractive. Lacrosse was only the beginning in his ability to play the field. The closer I get to him, the more he'll think he can use me for sex——not consistent sex, that would be too much of a commitment. More like one-time sex that he'll use to build his repertoire, and I'll fade from his memory to less than a number on his list.

I think this whole pursuit will be incredibly ironic. He interacts with me because he thinks he can use me for sex, and I try to get closer to him to see if he will try to use me for sex.

Amid the third week of second semester and in one particular business course, which I just so happened to be in, my professor read through a list of names of people who would be working together. An unfamiliar name rolled off her tongue, immediately following mine. My eyes had spent the past three weeks examining every single name tag in this room, and there was not one match. The professor handed me a slip of paper after class—a name, student ID number, and email sloppily sketched in thick gray pencil lead.

It turns out that name, student ID number, and email had yet to show up to class, which I learned about five days later and only after sending two follow-up emails. And about two more days after that, I learned that this name, student ID number, and email belonged to the most attractive man I have ever seen at this school.

My hair had gone unwashed for a few days, a quarter cup of grease spread throughout the roots of my blond hair. My clothes had also gone unwashed, leaving only the most ill-fitting black leggings that were two to three sizes too small. They were a decent match with my cherry red athletic crewneck, which was my only saving grace and not even that good of a saving grace.

I sat in my seat, looking like a packet of ketchup, which was found half-opened on the floor of a gas station, with french fries that were fresh out of the deep fryer growing on top of my head. And despite looking so flamboyantly ugly and unhygienic, a large hand with protruding veins from the wrist to the bases of the fingers extends itself towards me.

"It's nice to meet you."

Above the hand was a jawline only a diamond could cut with brown eyes that looked like they could love and betray at the same time, like a newborn puppy that looks at you while pissing on the new white carpet. They were comforting and mischievous like they wanted to keep their affairs secret.

"Are you—?"

We exchanged a smile before he turned back around, and that's how I knew I wanted Chad from Sigma Apple Pie to completely ruin my life.

It took me a bit to *actually* let him ruin my life.

As the course went on, and before the pandemic, we would meet in real life. His first impression of me was and forever will be that I was an unfortunate visible existence, so I tried to keep it that way. Meetings were strategically scheduled on hair follicle training days to keep the grease in my hair at its thickest and in the early evening so I could bring the sweat and bacteria I freshly acquired from track practice. If I actually put in effort, he might actually think I'm attractive, and that was the last thing I needed—not that he's ever been one to pay much attention to things.

Sometimes he would look at his watch and realize he had another meeting that already started. Other times, he would leave the meeting because he realized he had some unknown desire that wasn't being satisfied, and therefore couldn't maintain his presence in the meeting for a second longer. Yet often, as my four other team members and I sat at a small table in an already overcrowded dining hall, I could still feel his unwarranted gravitation towards me. I would look up from my computer and catch his eyes; he was either completely zoned out and simply facing my direction, which was highly likely, or I had captured his attention beneath my many layers of filth.

He's rushing a fraternity, but even if he wasn't, I would still associate him with Sigma Apple Pie, solely because of the way he carries himself. He carries around that general apathy that most fraternity brothers do. There's an interesting contrast between the way they portray themselves so mundanely yet light up with charisma as they cross paths in the overcrowded dining hall. It always seems like nothing matters, yet when certain people pass him it seems that everything does.

The slowly simmering heat between Chad and me warmed up one day when we both happened to be in the gym. I had to read a play for my acting class and decided to work out while doing so. It was a small gym attached to the dining hall with a few machines and weights. Chad was at the weights doing reverse flies with form so questionable that I stepped on the elliptical wearing a winter jacket with a script in hand, which, of course, happened to be the exact moment he noticed me, probably thinking something like, "Why the fuck is this unathletic loser wearing a winter jacket?"

Yet in this once again overcrowded space, he was still being pulled towards me. I could sense his eyes were near me, but they were not directly on me. He wanted to know what I was reading. The play in my hand intrigued him.

An even greater contrast in Chad is his inability to avoid impulse, yet his sheer predictability. I know that regardless of what I, or what anyone else does or says, his fate will play out and his final destination will be so predictable in retrospect. For example, Thursday night means he's getting drunk with the boys. We could schedule a business meeting, plan a picnic at Forest Park, or even a whole trip to France with minute-by-minute itineraries and prepurchased plane tickets, yet his unavoidable fate is getting drunk on Thursday with the boys, and it will come true. It's unclear as to how he would get out of any preestablished plans to do so, yet one impulse would lead to another—making him so ironically predictable.

His recklessness is so controlled, and I question how my overthinking makes me severely less predictable than him. I think through my every move to the point that I can't get a coffee without having a complete neural workout from trying to decide what to order, yet I'm quite unpredictable. I'm intrigued by how the under-thinker is significantly more predictable than the over.

He carries a certain façade, as every Chad from Sigma Apple Pie does. I know somewhere far beneath his surface are his goals, emotions, and aspirations, and I want nothing more than to be the one to find them. It's like trying to crack the piñata at a fellow four-year-old's birthday party. I think I can crack it open if I get close to it, but ultimately I can't overcome the fact I have the relative strength of a dying butterfly.

I like to think I think logical thoughts and have logically convinced myself I am incapable of making this work, yet I am still enthralled. I want to get closer and closer even though I cognitively know I don't have a chance.

Chad is going to be successful. I can just feel it even though it goes against all conventionality. No parents, adviser, book, or successful businessperson would ever tell you to live as impulsively as you can to achieve success. Yet one day, he'll walk to work on Wall Street wearing the latest edition of the same thousand-dollar coat that plagues our campus during the wintertime with his watch worth a year of tuition, and it'll be deemed "another day in the life."

He will probably achieve his success because one day he decided to go on a three-week bender with Connor, Tyler, and Jake (all from Sigma Apple) instead of doing whatever he was actually supposed to be doing. They'll go to a park, take three grams of magic mushrooms, and discover that human empathy exists. They'll each reach out to a person or two whom they have wronged with this newfound discovery that people have emotions. Feeling so inspired, they'll reach out to Brad—the CEO and founder of Sigma Apple—who then proceeds to give them promising careers, with the most promising of all going to Chad.

I think ahead too much, and I need to relax.

I want to know who Chad from Sigma Apple Pie really is, not just this stereotype that I use to convince myself that he's severely flawed and archetypical. A few days ago, I asked him to write an executive summary for our project, and what's even more surprising than the fact that he actually did is that the writing was impeccable—like, abnormally good with stylistically crafted words and phrases.

Maybe that's his thing. He's a passionate writer, hiding behind his apathy and lack of visible emotion. He conceals his greatest strengths from the world to cover up his fear of not being good enough. He brands himself as the frat boy business bro to avoid the potential of being destroyed by critiques, which he weighs all too heavily.

It's taken me awhile to realize it, but he's quiet and introverted. I think his mind is nowhere, but I almost believe his mind is everywhere. When he asks me questions in our video calls, I'm so thrown off by the specificity and intention. He asked me if I wanted to be an actress. How did he know?

The other day, I found myself on social media, and I typed in his name. If I'm going to be doing all of the work for our school project, I have rightfully earned a follow back.

Nothing was showing up. Did he block me?

I do some more digging and find his older sister's profile. She has hundreds of photos, dating almost a decade back. She went to our same school along with her other younger brother who appears to be a senior right now. That gives off very close-knit family vibes.

Her other brother is tagged in the photos while Chad is not, which means he probably doesn't have social media. That seems very off-brand with the person I assumed he was, but after discovering his writing, it's starting to make sense. He's somewhat of a minimalist and enjoys simplicity to some extent.

He was raised in Los Angeles and recently moved to New York. I already knew that though; Chad told me himself.

His sister seems a bit more nomadic, with photos in just about every major US city. She seems fun and like the type of person that certain people love to have around. She has strong opinions and stays true to her own bold aesthetic.

Her first photo with Chad isn't until 2017, and it's a photo of her at college graduation with him and their other brother. Chad appears to be holding either a vape or an iPod touch, and honestly neither would surprise me. If I would've seen this photo a few weeks ago, I definitely would've said vape, but now I'm leaning more toward iPod touch. He looks quite nerdy, especially with his boxy glasses frames, not at all how I would have envisioned his sixteen-year-old self.

A photo slideshow of Chad appears again on his seventeenth birthday. He's got the serious and intense gaze of a Capricorn sun, the innocent smile of a Libra moon, and the God complex glasses of an Aquarius mercury. His sister seems to really care about him; the fact that she went out of her way to post a birthday shoutout that he wouldn't even see is telling.

A few posts later, and his sister's feed begins to give off a different vibe—still fun and upbeat, yet drained and eerie. Her hair was entirely gone. She had Stage 3 leukemia.

Luckily, it's clear by her most recent posts that she had conquered it. Yet throughout it all, her family appeared to be a crucial part of her life. From the aforementioned birthday post to her most recent, Chad appeared to mature significantly. Even in her next post with him, he had already ditched the smile and the boxy glasses and developed his signature look of apathy. He now looked much more like the preppy lax bro who extended his hand to a gas station ketchup packet.

Each photo of him makes me feel like I know him less and less. He was supposed to be a generic hot man who played lacrosse and rushed a frat, but now he's a mysterious and compassionate writer who is greatly misunderstood.

There's clearly a story in him, and I'm too invested to back out.

# CHAPTER 7

# DELMAR

———

I use the opportunity of my shared online class with Chad to get dressed up—aka a plain-colored t-shirt with mascara, a bit of highlighter, and a neutral liquid lipstick—so he notices me, and it appears to be working because he starts texting me individually outside of our team group chat, which has me elated. But since class is only held one to two times a week, I have to find other things to do in the meantime.

Every other day of lockdown, I walk around campus aimlessly for hours at a time, trying to figure out what to do with my endless void of existence. Between walks, I'll make whipped coffee with warm sink water in a plastic bowl and scroll through my phone for hours at a time. I might even start making dancing videos, but that'll be my last resort.

Today, after online shopping for clothes I will never buy, but with my computer camera on so I could get participation credit for my classes, I decide to take a walk toward Delmar, the infamous Delmar with restaurants and small businesses, where everyone at my school goes to get an ice cream float that they will not actually eat but will certainly post on every social media they have.

Hidden between the acres of gothic architecture on my campus that screams elitism from miles and miles away, there is a nice concrete walkway that trails through a small neighborhood to take me there.

The median household income at my school is slightly under $300,000, making it the second wealthiest student body in the United States (Peck 2020). Being contained in the atmosphere of such monstrous wealth creates an illusion from the rest of the society, and it's a phenomenon often called the "bubble." The people around me are much unlike the rest of society, and cognitively I know it, but consciously I don't. Others' high expectations and unwarranted fears of not getting into prestigious investment banks rub off on me, and I forget there are much greater struggles in this world. Any step out of the bubble and into the city is refreshing.

Whenever I talk to my friends from elsewhere, I forget their world is not reflective of mine. I remember being shocked when one of my friends told me she wasn't looking for summer internships after her first college summer. I am so far detached from reality.

So when I take a step off campus and onto the gateway, I feel relieved. The gateway takes me to a walkway with rows of houses on each side, a world closer to reality while still being so far from it.

I imagine the houses on each side of the gateway aren't particularly spectacular to most of my student body. They're middle- to upper-middle-class homes, some are only one level, not something the median student at my institution would own, and they are nice houses, but the stark contrast between the $8 billion endowment a few meters back makes them feel underwhelming—makes them feel like the average American reality.

It's the type of contrast that makes me forget that in the world's wealthiest nation, forty-six million people cannot even afford necessary health care (Vaidya 2021).

I pass the houses are restaurants and shops. Occasionally, there are unhoused people that make me feel like this is reality at its fullest. The one singular person, or small group of people, I see makes me fall into the fallacy of thinking that some lives are unfortunate, but it's on the individual level, and there is little anyone could do. It makes me erroneously feel that, surely, they are one of the outliers in this world, and there are bound to be outliers in a world of billions of people, so the rest of the world must be a very fair and happy place. I continue, surrounded by the neon lights and vintage stores.

The vibe is very modern with a unique twist: a classic street of restaurants but with fun art displaced throughout, and there's a Starbucks. It feels true to the city and irreplicable elsewhere.

The ice cream float diner, the one with the floats that live on social media, is next to a barbecue place. As a vegan, I've been there more times than I care to recall, and I've sat and watched my friends eat plates of meat while I drank an iced water and pretended like I wasn't starving.

I could spend all day roaming Delmar, and it would be a good, fun day. I could go vintage thrift shopping, support some small business, and take cute photos with a neon peacock in the background. I could get so caught up in the ups of the Delmar sidewalk that I would never think to cross the next street over.

The next street over is the reality that's been strategically cast away from the common eye. From the side that stems from the walkway to its opposite, there is a twenty-year difference in life expectancy (Householder 2017). Twenty feet over from the neon peacock is life at its realest. The ritzy artwork coating the streets of Delmar fades to concrete and lifelessness.

I've never walked that side of Delmar, but with the shutdown of Earth, everything is lifeless, and I no longer find myself distracted by the life that once was. I cross over at the intersection with the Mission Taco, and I walk. There isn't much other than a chicken shack, and it's clear it has been drained of all resources that could possibly make it flourish, leaving it a concrete desert and a structured obstacle to mobility.

The homes aren't houses; they are apartment complexes. They are coated in a nice brown on the outside and are plain enough to not stand out, but not enough to stay hidden. Perhaps that's to deceive the aimless wanderer from truly realizing the stark difference from one street to the next.

The complexes tower above them, with square windows pointing to the side of luxury. I wonder if people who live on the top floor can look out and see the privilege they weren't given.

People, only streets over, are struggling to be alive as I make my way back to my dorm with my multi-thousand-dollar mattress given to me courtesy of my university.

# CHAPTER 8

# LOST IN SPACE

———

Despite the inequality taking place almost literally right outside my window, there's very little I can do at this very point in time, so I let my boredom (and hormones) take the reins for the rest of lockdown. Chad from Sigma Apple Pie is my only motivation to get through school. I, who months ago would've cried—and definitely did cry on multiple occasions—at a 75 percent on an exam, would only be phased by a flat 0, and only moderately phased if it would affect Chad's perception of myself. So much of my life has gone toward academic validation, yet now it feels so empty and meaningless. The letters on my transcript that once defined my entire existence are now as weighty as the clouds.

My first exam of my first semester was for Calculus 3. The content had been pretty doable, and after three consecutive nights doing practice problems at the library, I walked into the testing center with confidence. There was no sweat on my hands, which was quite uncommon. I sat in a small wooden desk in the back of the room ready to take this test as though I were a Capricorn fighting through the perils of life. The digital clock projected to the front wall struck 6:30 a.m. My fingers flipped the first page of the booklet to begin. The content was completely foreign. The sweat on my hands grew thicker and thicker until the pencil was starting to slip. I began to cry, which evolved into a bawl and led to a panic attack. I pulled up my navy sweatshirt to cover the lower half of my face, an attempt to cancel out any noise from my hysteria.

The test takers around me probably found it ironically hilarious, as do I, in retrospect. The thought of proctors witnessing me crying to then go home and wonder if they're paid enough is kind of funny. At the time, however, I left the testing center with a deep shadow of sadness, which followed me for the next few days, weeks, and honestly months. I got a 33 percent, and I had never felt like a larger waste of space. My intellect on paper was everything; I was absolutely nothing without it.

To rebound from this test, which was succeeded by a waterfall of never-ending failure condensed into one semester, I enrolled in seven classes for the spring: Data Structures & Algorithms, Logic and Discrete Mathematics, Financial Accounting, Foundations of Business, Management Communication, Acting II, and, unfortunately, Calculus 3 for the second time. It should be known that I didn't fail the first time. I just thought my GPA defined my self-worth. I've never been a great test taker, which I hate to admit, yet with online learning, nothing feels real and everything seems meaningless.

The truth of whether there is meaning in life has never truly haunted me. It was one of those deep, out-of-pocket topics that gets brought up in conversation with close friends, but now, I'm a nihilist and aspiring existentialist. Nothing actually matters, and I wish to use that fact as a form of enlightenment, but instead it's destructive.

It's starting to get nice outside, and I am starting to see the light at an unknown position of a tunnel that was only supposed to be two weeks long. I go on lots of walks.

There's been an interesting evolution of outdoor walking during the pandemic. At the first shutdown of nonessential stores, no one was outside. It was quite apocalyptic, and even the mightiest villains were afraid of innocent pedestrians. Yet about a week later, more people were outside, and walking seemed to be a shared pastime among us all.

About two weeks in, St. Louis County implemented a stay-at-home order. I don't think anyone really knew what that entailed, myself included, but it was interpreted as a game of human bumper cars. Seeing someone else on a walk meant turning in another direction and walking another way. Comparable to being in a room with every past hookup, "We fucked once and never talk about it" became the vibe of the great outdoors.

I primarily go to Forest Park, which is an easy walk from campus. It's very much a city park with well-groomed grass, a golf course, and manmade structures within every angle of sight. There are a few dirt trails meant to simulate the natural world, but even there, one's eyes cannot escape the monstrous city buildings surrounding them. It makes the nature of it very pseudo, but it's still a nice walk.

I tend to walk around for two and a half hours at a time. I've lost about ten pounds without cognitively trying. My phone stays in my dorm room because I know that if I brought it, I'd be glued to the news and the COVID tracker— neither of which reveal any truly new information, which is why I'd rather roam around with my own thoughts, as dark and anxiety inducing as they may be.

There isn't really much to think about. I find it difficult to make goals when life is so variable, which really only leaves me to think of the past, the Dichotomy, and Chad from Sigma Apple Pie.

The past is hard to think about. It's weird and awkward, and it's just so different from who I am now and who I will be in a year. Eighteen years invested into an identity that ceases to exist is unsettling. I have no idea who I am, and it feels like the past can't help me.

My small high school in rural Minnesota loved me more than the students could ever admit. As a speech captain, band geek, mathlete, and economics researcher, I was the smart, inquisitive student that every teacher wanted in class. I had a few close friends and was equally liked and disliked by my peers.

I was shy and awkward yet very opinionated and confident. Boys were mean and slandered me in their group chats, so I outperformed them in every regard. I didn't really care if I was liked as long as I was the best at everything.

That didn't really translate well at a college full of people who are only the best at everything. Clubs were competitive. Academics were worse. I had nothing but the unstable grounds of my anxiety to work with. Compared to others, I was not the best and it was actually impossible for me to be.

People on the track team think I am strange. I'm painfully aware of the vibe I give off to people. It's sort of like dramatic irony. They don't know I know they think I'm odd, but I am so very aware. Being a thrower on the track team comes with a level of insecurity. Everyone around you is half your size and audibly insecure about being too large. Small talk feels antagonistic.

The best memory I have is the absolute exhilaration I felt leaving campus and driving four and a half hours to meet some random guy that messaged me while I was in high school. That in itself is ironically funny. The girl with so much anxiety that she couldn't drink a singular sip of alcohol because it might take away the time she needed to work on school randomly decided to drive to a different state for a DM slider. Maybe that says something about the identity that I cannot define. I'm curious and adventurous, perhaps.

The Dichotomy and I still talk. We are good friends. He doesn't quite mind this void of time as he and his family are very close. He's bored, but who isn't? The other day, he sent me a straight face selfie with his acceptance to Columbia University. Yes, THE Columbia University. He had already gotten into the University of Chicago and was disappointed after getting rejected by Stanford. I am happy for him since he is not happy for himself.

He is by no means my soulmate in any regard. Yet there is some out-of-world force that seems to have brought us into coexistence. He likes to talk about politics and world history while being a die-hard sports fan who owns "Saturdays are for the boys" merchandise and messages random girls he thinks are attractive. He's such a dichotomy, and I crave his unique sense of humor and snarky disposition.

The line between platonic and romantic attraction is paper thin. The after-midnight phone and video calls excite me, making the platonic attraction increasingly stronger. To crave the energy of another and want them in your life is at the heart of both, and I tend to get them confused. But he and I are not meant to be romantically involved, and any inkling otherwise is my own deception.

When it comes to Chad from Sigma Apple Pie, however, there is no confusion. I am incapable of restricting my attraction to platonic. Thinking of him keeps my walks interesting because I live for the chase. He is close to my life while being so far out of my league that I can endlessly plot ways to get myself so asymptotically close that not even a nanoscope can see if I truly pulled him or not.

My relationship with Chad from Sigma Apple Pie is my first paradox, which I must have inadvertently manifested through thinking so much about the Dichotomy. He's the obvious player; I'm the obvious playee. Yet beneath the obvious, the playee subverts the dynamic by using the player to feed her own curiosity.

He thinks highly of me. If he knew that I got a 33 percent on the calc test, the entire image he constructed of me would crumble to dust. He thinks I'm some perfectionist that has everything figured out with a clear, conventional plan to achieve what I want. Failure does not exist in my world as far as he is concerned. He has no clue I use our course as a source of procrastination because the busy work lets me delay my active thoughts while still feeling productive.

Talking to Chad is sort of like a makeshift acting boot camp to account for the lessons I missed when I was younger. I am consciously aware of the way he perceives me, and everything I do in his eyes is consistent with that image. From his point of view, I am confident, focused, and put together. Maybe I actually am, and I let my own fears consume me until all I see is that I'm not. Regardless, I have an intrinsic way of acting around Chad, which means any efforts to get to know him on a deeper level have to be consistent with that. There has to be a certain maturity and confidence to reach that asymptotic proximity.

"Olivia."

I look up from my notebook during our Zoom call.

"Have you ever been to Big Daddy's?"

The Wi-Fi is too good to blame for my lack of motion. Big Daddy's is a local St. Louis nightclub. There are many mixed opinions, but the general consensus is to be blackout drunk before you walk in the door.

I ignore the question. Despite being in yes-or-no format, I cannot deal with the consequences of either answer.

"Olivia, you should come to Big Daddy's once COVID is over."

I force a laugh. What the actual fuck. Does he actually find me attractive? People often say things they don't mean. He definitely doesn't mean it, and if I say something, he'll think something like, "Omg, why does the greasy bathroom floor ketchup packet with a little mascara and highlighter actually think I want to hang out with her?" To which I won't be able to comeback from, and my great plan will be ruined, so I ignore him.

My rejection to his request of a yes-or-no answer to his question drove him so mad that he messages me the next day.

"You are actually the best"

"How can I ever repay you?"

I look at my lock screen and do a fifteen-times take. HE texted ME. My master plan is falling into place, and I'm hardly even trying.

"haha, thank you"

"it's alright though, don't worry"

The notion of "playing hard to get" is childish and immature, so it should be noted that was not my intention. The timing just doesn't seem right, and with summer quickly approaching, any conversation about coursework is too transient to pursue. However, I will say, I am very aware of reciprocity, the psychological principle used by many marketers, which states that people feel morally obliged to return favors. By him not being able to return the favor, he will have a certain underlying uncomfortableness that can only be resolved if he interacts with me. I will be living on his mind and in his subconscious until he believes he has repaid me.

Summer is where I believe the Sigma scavenge shall gain some traction. With the pandemic going on, plus his recent move to upstate New York, who else is he going to be talking to? Although we will be over one thousand miles apart, distance no longer feels like a factor for closeness.

***

Summer is when the notion of performative activism became opaque by "Blackout Tuesday"—a trend of posting a black square that could potentially block streams of pertinent information as a way of boosting one's personal "wokeness" regarding police brutality and the tragic murder of George Floyd. Things need to change and posting infographics on my Instagram story isn't enough.

I know I said there's nothing I can do right now, but maybe I was wrong. With the upcoming election season, there has to be something I can do. Perhaps, politics can be my next pursuit—a side hustle to the Sigma operation.

Alexandria Ocasio-Cortez's documentary *Knock Down the House* is at the top of my watch list. It'll probably give me much needed inspiration, so I should watch it. I bring my computer outside along with a pencil and notebook. Maybe one day I could apply to intern for her, and in that case, I will have direct quotes available for my cover letter.

About twenty-five minutes into the documentary, the St. Louis arch flashes in the background of a street view. The scene transitions to a group of three people talking in a room. One of them leads the conversation.

"We're still number one in murder per capita. We're in the top three in African American poverty. . . For African Americans who are almost 50 percent of the district to have a Black congressman as long as they have had and still have not made any significant gains. . ."

He continues talking and turns to the woman in the room.

"If change is going to happen in St. Louis, this is our moment."

The scene fades out and a screen with the text "CORI BUSH, RUNNING FOR CONGRESS IN MISSOURI'S FIRST DISTRICT" replaces it.

I close out the movie and enter "Cori Bush" into another tab.

She first ran for Senate in 2016 where she lost to Jason Kander in the Democratic primary by a margin of 56.6 percent (Ballotpedia 2016). Cori fought back in 2018, running against William Lacy Clay for representative of Missouri's first district, gaining significant traction but still trailing behind by a margin of 19.8 percent (Ballotpedia 2018). Now, she is running again in 2020, entirely grassroots funded, still against Lacy Clay, who inherited the seat from his father after thirty-two years of leadership, ingraining the last name

"Clay" into the minds of the St. Louis people for the past fifty-two years (Allen 2020). She is once again fighting against generations of accrued nostalgia and mounds of corporate funding with limited funding of her own and her undeniable commitment to the people.

She's the change St. Louis needs. And with my intellect combined with my propensity for competition, especially after seeing inequality firsthand on my walks through Delmar, I know I would be a great asset on her team.

I head back inside and decide to take a break from my computer. My favorite neon pink sports bra taunts me by hanging over the edge of one of my dresser drawers. I wonder what Chad would think if he saw me in that neon pink sports bra. Wait. I can make that happen.

I replace my current attire with the strip of neon pink and grab a pair of dark gray shorts from the floor, which, after a smell test, I deem are safe. I take a selfie (actually seventeen selfies) until finally settling on one that looks cute. I add a digital sticker of the arch with the caption "in paradise."

"damn, I wish I were there
right now"

He replies almost instantaneously.

"come to stl"

My excitement takes the lead, and I send the invitation to my city without thinking.

Minutes go by and I'm beginning to wonder if I read his message wrong. Maybe he really just likes St. Louis, and I'm so self-absorbed that I thought his wanting to be here had something to do with me. Maybe he isn't even into women, yet because of overtly heteronormative frat culture, I just assumed he was. Maybe he was just being nice all this time and really wants nothing to do with me. That's a likely scenario. He seems like a nice guy in a non "pick-me" way.

Then he finally responds.

"I'm planning on coming sometime
in the next month, we should
definitely meet up"

Wait. How was that so easy? There's nooo way. That was too easy. This is fake. How do I even reply to that without spewing out my passionate love that is unfortunately in the body of an incredibly awkward eighteen-year-old girl?

"yeah, just lmk"

He's going to see my text abbreviation and think, "Wow, she's so chill and cool." I just know it. My life is mirroring the unexpected chaos of the world around me because, despite my interactions with Chad being incredibly well thought out, I never actually believed a message like this would happen.

I ride this amorous high while I research how to be involved in the Cori Bush campaign.

I'll be canvassing tomorrow at 9:00 a.m. and maybe I'll be pregnant "sometime in the next month."

# CHAPTER 9

# THE CAMPAIGN

———

Eight a.m. is the earliest I've woken in months, so Cori really does have a way of defying all odds. Yesterday, I sent her a direct message and she replied with an address, which, according to my navigation software, is a spacious parking lot about fifteen minutes away, so the possibilities of today's adventure are increasingly endless. She has less than ten thousand followers on Instagram. She isn't necessarily "famous" by a conventional standard, but I feel more starstruck by her than I would if Taylor Swift data mined the web for my phone number and invited me to her childhood home in Pennsylvania.

Cori will share her story with anyone who asks, but her biography is readily available on her website. Cori Bush grew up about twenty minutes away, right outside Ferguson, Missouri. When unarmed teenager Michael Brown was murdered by police in 2014, Cori arrived at the brutal fight for racial justice to—simply—do her job. As an ordained pastor, mother of two, and a registered nurse, she arrived at the scene to "lend a hand as a nurse," completely unaware of the path her compassion and charisma would take her.

"I wasn't trying to become an activist," she often claims.

The majority of her life spent in one of the most broken parts of an already corrupt system finally became too much when she saw others experiencing the same burdens she had been carrying for the past thirty-eight years. She's faced evictions, homelessness, racism, sexual assault, physical abuse, and fell severely ill with COVID after serving as a frontline nurse amid the pandemic.

So it's quite simple: Cori doesn't want anyone to ever endure the same hardships she did. Her humility and selflessness are unmatched, so I could not care less if her current social clout is relatively unextraordinary because she is so authentic and wonderful, and SHE replied to ME!

I'm omw to 75 North Oaks Plaza. I head past Delmar and into the heart of a once-prosperous area that was drained of all resources and forced to continue living. Past the first set of brown apartment complexes is a small open field that leads to an intersection with a "Cash Gold" store and a "Grand Opening" of a fish mart, both of which look completely dead and locationally incapable of coming to life. The drive continues the pattern of brown apartment complexes followed by small fields of dead grass that lead to run-down businesses.

The actual address is a little office in a strip mall. It's sandwiched between a Save A Lot and a clothing store and about two hundred feet behind a McDonald's. The inside is the size of a small pop-up boutique with the thinnest layer of dark gray carpet coating a firm surface. There is a desk to the right with a cool-looking man sitting in front of it. He has voluminous curly black hair with a black-and-white camouflage mask. His water bottle is pink, blue, and yellow, and his baggy oversized tank top with stylistic black jeans must have been carefully selected from a thrift store. Nice.

There are four of those classic wooden fold tables pushed together with the standard gray-brown chairs to match. The walls are coated with maps, district outlines, and activism posters, many of which are wonderfully hand drawn and crafted for protest purposes, yet a basic yellow poster with "CLOSE THE WORKHOUSE" in white and black text stands out the most.

The workhouse in question refers to the St. Louis Medium Security Institution, a place that puts people awaiting trial into cages and forces them to produce labor, not because they have been proven guilty, but because they can't afford their fines. According to the Close The Workhouse Campaign, upholding the workhouse has historically cost St. Louis taxpayers $16 million per year—once again a seemingly small use of taxpayer dollars that could go toward universal health care or other services for the public good. So many policies miss the public eye, and if it weren't for the beeline yellow of the poster, this would have missed mine.

A few feet in front of the poster wall, there is a yellow couch, which was definitely secondhand, with a few more tables and desks. This place is the definition of ballin' on a budget. It has everything that's needed and not much more; strategic minimalism at its finest.

Cori Bush isn't here at the moment because—in addition to being a single mother, ordained pastor, and running a campaign to take down generations of acquired nostalgia and millions of dollars from large corporations—she's a full-time nurse during a global pandemic.

The cool-looking man gets up from his desk and hands me a stack of orange and purple flyers with Cori's photo and policies on it. He hands me a Post-it note with an intersection of two streets penciled in. I am to go to that intersection and use a canvassing app to retrieve the addresses to which I will dole this stack. Got it.

The intersection is in a medium-sized neighborhood, right near the initial tragedy that started Cori's unintentional political debut. The houses are all one story, and each is the same rectangular shape with a different shade of brown or white, plus the occasional red. This is not a privileged area, and I can imagine that too many of the residents are living below the poverty line. I walk up to the first house to hand out the first flyer. I have my mask on, and to be extra COVID safe, I jam the flyer in the small crack between the door and the frame. I ring the doorbell and jolt back to maintain six feet of distance.

A man opens the door. He looks me up and down—not in a creepy, "I think she's attractive" type of way, but in a confused, startled, and "there's no possibility this girl has anything good to say" type of way. The flyer falls to the doorstep, and he picks it up before resuming eye contact.

"Hi!" There is a long script on my phone, which is in my hand, but it feels unnatural, so I freeze.

"What are you doing?"

The perfect cue for me to talk.

"I'm campaigning for Cori Bush. Can we count on your vote for August the fourth?" Straight to the point.

"We'll see." He looks down at the flyer and back at me as though he's in shock that I have a moral compass. "Have a nice day, ma'am."

He closes the door and goes back inside. I'll consider it a "neutral undecided" for the records.

The rest of the interactions are similar if even anything at all. Most people don't answer their doors, which is alright with me and probably alright for the campaign considering I don't know how to talk to people. As long as they get the flyer, and I make an honest attempt to talk to them, the message is relayed, and my job is done. Although seemingly unexciting, it's so exhilarating to be a part of something so much greater than myself (and something that keeps me away from Chad for the time being).

I go back to the office, and I am determined to be as annoying as possible to be a part of this campaign. I'm about to become the equivalent of an unrequited love interest that sends new messages before even giving the chance to reject the previous. According to the official office hours, they close at 9:00 p.m., and from now until then, I am cemented to this thin gray carpet and they cannot get rid of me. I will be the first thing the cool-looking man sees when they open at 9:00 a.m., and I will continue this pattern until I am officially welcomed onto the team.

"Hi! My name is Olivia. I just got done with handing out flyers, and I was wondering if there are any other ways that I can help out." I approach the cool man. He extends his hand to shake mine and he introduces himself.

"I'm Adrastos, nice to meet you!"

He walks me over to large cardboard boxes filled with the same flyers I had just handed out.

"If you could create stacks of one hundred, that would be great!"

And so, I create stacks of one hundred. Exciting, I know. I'm honestly cool with doing whatever because someone has to count stuff for this campaign to run. I just think it's kind of funny. Like, this is a pretty big deal that impacts the lives of millions of people and it's crazy to think that paper in a thin layer of wax could ultimately be the difference.

Minutes of counting paper stacks leads to hours of counting other things like office supplies and voter statistics, which continues until the sun begins to set.

"I'll see you tomorrow!" I wave goodbye to Adrastos as I walk out the door. I strategically implant myself in his mind, and he knows I will return.

I arrive the next day at 8:40 a.m., twenty minutes before they open, but I can—and will—sit it out in my car. It's alright. I would wait seventeen hours if it meant I would be the first thing Adrastos sees when he unlocks the door.

My strategy worked, and this day is similar to the previous. No canvassing so far, just necessary administrative tasks. I meet some more people on the campaign and gain some traction in my goal to implant myself.

About an hour in, a guy my age walks through the door and turns toward Adrastos. He walks with a sense of urgency as though he is as desperate as I to be a part of this campaign.

"Hi." He stops himself. Great start. "I just graduated college. I've been working part-time in my parent's basement. I'm from New Jersey. . ." He continually pauses between each sentence as though each one is going to be the one that does some magic. "When I was in college, I played baseball. I started managing their social media. I just saw one of Cori's tweets go viral, and I immediately hopped in my car and drove over one thousand miles to be here."

Alas, the magical sentence rolls of his tongue, making this next pause hit different. How could Adrastos possibly reject someone that just drove over one thousand miles and had no alternate plan? I'm glad he spoke up 'cause that was a pretty solid "in" that I can easily freeload off of.

"Would you like to be an official intern?" I hear Adrastos ask the man, and I walk ten feet over to their congregation faster than I have ever walked ten feet. Immediately after baseball boy's obvious yes, I selfishly interject myself: "I'd actually love to intern too!" Adrastos nods his head. It worked.

The three of us come together and shuffle through forms like one small, happy family. I never knew using a pen could be so exciting.

***

A few weeks in, and the work gets more challenging with time. COVID spikes and fears of a second lockdown increase tension in the office.

My computer skills became public knowledge faster than I intended. But honestly, I find interacting with voters the most challenging of all.

Phone banking for a US progressive takes every last ounce of humanism one has and runs it over three hundred times with a monster truck that has acid-covered knives for tires. The conversations go from a meek "Hi, how are you?" to an abrasive thread of threats and anger within seconds.

The casual conversations aren't much better. They highlight the pure misinformation sent out by those who think politics is a game like checkers, those who think there are two opponents of equal deservingness and merit, and it should be up to manipulative strategy between them to make the other lose. Also, it really doesn't help when the name "Cori Bush," or just "Bush" in general, sounds like a standard hateful old white man that thinks climate change is proven false every time the temperature drops below forty in the spring.

My favorite is when people say they heard that Cori is neither a nurse nor a pastor. We then go around in circles with a game of "well, actually. . ." and "but I heard. . ." People hang onto lies backed by absolutely zero evidence the way a sloth clings to a cecropia tree. Literally, so fun (major sarcasm intended).

Cori is doing a virtual event tonight. At 7:30 p.m., she'll be going live on social media. We've had a little over nineteen hundred people register, which obviously isn't a lot in the grand scheme of life, but quite impressive for a political candidate with no fame or privilege to support her. Thus far, Cori has been doing virtual "neighborhood tours" with only a handful of people at a time. Tonight could be crucial for gaining votes.

We move the couch in the back to make the space look super professional for the livestream. Someone brought in a podium, and we decorated the wall behind it with "Cori for Congress" and activism posters. The other intern places the "CLOSE THE WORKHOUSE" poster at the visible top—it's universally captivating.

Cori is wearing her signature shade of royal purple. She hasn't said much as she's paced around the office, but I just know she's going to nail this. It's nearly impossible to listen to Cori and think, *Meh, that was alright.*

The energy in the room feels much like being an adolescent on a sports team that's just made it to a championship game. There is a magnet in my chest that is moving me toward a triumphant possibility that once seemed unattainable. There is something coming, and I can just feel it.

Cori steps onto the podium. The professional LED lights, movie camera, and about seventeen hundred pairs of eyes are on her. I gulp. I can barely form coherent sentences in front of one person. That's a lot of people.

Luckily, she is not me. She starts speaking, and I never want her to stop. I can feel my soul moving with every syllable as she tells her story. She's told the same story over and over throughout her candidacy, yet it never gets even remotely old. The power behind her speech is motivating beyond words, and if she speaks long enough, I might get up from my seat and become the next Greta Thunberg.

Behind the mic, I hear faint whispers from other livestream facilitators.

"She just hit fifty thousand," one of them says so faintly yet energetically, enough that I can discern the windy voice.

That's obviously much more than anticipated, but I am not surprised. The energy, drive, and passion she brings is unmatched.

"She's almost at two hundred thousand," the same whisper returns before the end of her speech.

Within thirty minutes, Cori Bush had managed to reach thousands and thousands of people.

Cori really does have a way of defying all odds.

# CHAPTER 10

# 3:00 A.M.

---

Is there really anything more exciting than a progressive garnering traction against a fifty-two-year political dynasty that, even at its lowest, is still a relative high point of a murderous colonial empire?

Objectively, not much.

Subjectively, I am eighteen and can be quite irrational because two days ago, and one night after Cori's livestream, Chad sent me a photo with a St. Louis digital sticker, (very similar to the one that I had sent him weeks ago). I shouldn't be excited at all because he has his location on, and he's actually been here for the past four days and waited two whole days to tell me. He's been quite nomadic throughout the city, probably bouncing between parties and other women who are just as naïve as I, but I feel as though I am Cori Bush—in all her glory—stepping off the podium after flawlessly livestreaming to thousands of people, internalizing the view count and accepting the future for its infinite potential.

The future only really has potential if I meddle with fate, so I turn my location on too; my cartoon figure joins his on a cartoon city map. Will he take the bait that will lead to his requited obsession? Will he open the app, see my cute cartoonish figure in blue jeans and maroon high-tops, finding himself growing more obsessed with the pixels that move relative to his? Will he find himself drawn to discovering more about the #girlboss who did all his homework for him? Hopefully.

He'll see my blonde figure inching across his screen. He'll find himself zooming in, wanting to know what kind of coffee I like to drink as he sees my figure at the Starbucks on Delmar. He probably thinks I like my coffee hot. I'm too mature and driven to be indulging in iced sugar. I bet he likes his coffee hot. Beneath his crazy party frat boy nature, he's a bit serious and sees life as a battle, which is the way he knows best as a Capricorn sun.

I bet he likes his coffee hot because he is a writer. Most writers like their coffee hot. It's just the vibe. He probably brews his own and drinks it from a dark ceramic mug that he washes once every few months. He grabs his full glass and brings it to his desk to write a story, but what's he writing about? When he's writing a love interest, who comes to mind? What memories is he using to draw inspiration?

Probably not me. At least not yet. Has he ever been in love? I can't imagine him in love.

He's quite emotionally mature, and not just for "boys his age," because that would be the equivalent of saying that a finance bro has a small ego for a finance bro, which means close to nothing. His emotional maturity and apathy sort of fuse together and into an abstraction. He seems like he knows how to control his emotions, but I don't know if he even has emotions to control.

If someone were to profess their love to him, he would probably say something like "cool." He'd probably console the other for his lack of reciprocation, and never would he think to make it into mockery. He isn't that type of person. His absence of thoughts never manifests through making fun of others.

I can't imagine him watching sports, especially football. I could see a less mainstream sport like skiing or swimming slightly capturing his attention, but no more than slightly. He doesn't have the angry fervor it takes to be a true sports fan.

What does he even like to talk about? My conversations with him are blurry because I literally have an intense internal panic every single time he talks to me. He likes books and writing, but there's no way that's what he's talking about with his fellow frat bros. Maybe he is just as gossipy as the rest. If I can make him think I'm some very well put-together perfection, he can certainly make me think the same about him as well. But I'm usually never wrong about people, especially guys. They're just too easy to read.

According to his cartoon figure on the app's map, Chad is now at Jeni's Ice Cream in the Central West End, which is a very cute spot that I'd recommend just for the aesthetic. The shop is a blend of neutral shades and hues of neon with those old vintage style lights that hang from the ceiling. I envision Chad and I going there in some other dimension and universe that isn't this one. He wouldn't spend more than five and a half seconds looking at the menu and would order something basic like mint or dark chocolate. The rest of his time would be spent looking at the golden locks of the girl eight inches below him. Her eyes are fixated on the three dairy-free options as she narrows it down to cold brew with coconut cream and caramel pecan sticky buns.

I envision us leaving the shop and walking around the neighborhood, past the chess arena and into the rows and rows of old-money architecture. Chad drops something at some point, probably his wallet. He doesn't realize he's dropped his wallet until we have finished traversing past houses and we come across the Gaslight Theatre. Next door there are clear glass windows and dark blue lighting. An electric piano and microphone are showcased at the heart of the bar. It's a quiet night, but the potential energy is radiant. We look at each other, knowing we'd be back someday when it is far livelier, and the energy can catalyze our ever-growing fantasy.

We dash off into the night to run away together. He grabs my purple hand that can't circulate blood because I have severe Raynaud's, brings it above my head, and spins me around like I am wearing a voluminous Cinderella dress. Our feet skid the surface of the concrete; we are moving so fast. We make it to the nearest gas station and pick out an assortment of salt and sugar. I grab sour gummies and snack crackers while he directs blue raspberry ice into foam cups. We go to pay, and that's when he realizes he's lost his wallet.

We walk back with heavy footsteps, more somber than we should be. He grabs the brown leather box with his debit card and license, which is now covered in dirt and gravel. Maybe all we ever are is kinetic energy, and not the type that moves mountains and planes, but the type that comes and goes with the wind and stands on nothing in the slightest substantial.

I need to be careful how much I check his location since I have mine on too. Not that I am actually following him physically, but if his curiosity becomes even half as strong as mine, he will see my activity status and think I have no life since I am checking the app every thirty seconds.

I should contact him. We never officially made plans to meet up, and most obviously I want to see him.

"Hey, what are you doing later?"

The word "later" may have been my greatest mistake. "Later" is too ambiguous.

"The brothers are throwing a party,
how late do you stay up?"

I want to see him so badly, and I do not want to do anything that would prevent him from not wanting to see me.

"5:00 a.m."

That was such a lie. He knows it's bullshit.

"no way"

He thinks I'm too put together, and this time he's kind of right.

"no seriously, like I just love staying
up really late"

That part was true, I do love the night. The 5:00 a.m. part was a bit on the extreme side, but whatever works.

"okieee, i'll hyu later if im free"

Ah, the classic response of a soon-to-be college sophomore. I've heard the never-ending tales of the very archetype that is "'i'll hyu later if im free," yet this is my first immersive experience. Bonus points to him for adding his own unique twist.

The day fades to night, and I have yet to be "hit up." I take a long walk beneath the night sky. Normally my feelings about people are correct but they never are with him. I feel so awkward and cringe and overtly strange around him that I long predicted he thought I was too awkward and cringe and overtly strange and would therefore never even give me the time of day. Yet here we are, potentially about to meet up on our own willing accord.

"R u up?"

His message finally comes in at 1:47 a.m.

"Yes lol, what's up?"

"Do you want to hang in like an hour?"

"sure"

I strategically pick the most casual and least enthusiastic "yes."

"okay, i'm at—"

He sends me his location as if I didn't already have it.

I tell him I'll be there at 3:00 a.m., which is another universal attribute of a classic Chad from Sigma. From any outsider's perspective, I am most definitely getting played, but I strongly object. We are two astral bodies, moving with the universe in a way that our physical shells could not match within the realms of societal existence. And in other words, he is still a ploy in my heartless curiosity project.

I'm pretty sure he isn't sober. Not that his messages were particularly weird or off putting, but it's night and well. . . he's a Chad from Sigma.

"I think I'm here"

I send him the message even though I know I'm here because there's an opaque bubble around our cartoon selves on the map, signifying the same geographic location.

He comes down from the apartment in a white T-shirt with blue jeans and high-top black shoes. If I were to search "outfit" on my phone right now, a direct match would probably appear. He's really tall, which I already knew, but it's surprising because he just doesn't seem like the type that would be really tall. He doesn't have a "tall personality" because a "tall personality" is one that is overtly douchey or awkward, and he isn't really either, so it just seems unfitting for him (definitely not complaining though).

"Hey." He somehow fits in my relatively short sedan, but it's like the equivalent of seven clowns.

"How's it going?"

It's going well for him, or so he claims. He's spent his summer in Westchester with his family in a place too small to avoid the pressing bicker. Not that that argument is necessarily a hardship as much as an annoyance, but he did mention it. He's been reading Russian literature and listening to podcasts. I bet he's been writing too but didn't feel connected enough to tell me. Telling people you write takes courage because all of a sudden people expect you to be the most fantastic writer and then you fear writing because you're so afraid that each and every word will not be perfect and you will be the biggest failure. I would love to read his writing though, the roughest and most candid of drafts. His works that are so objectively messy that I couldn't summarize them if I tried. I just want to know what's on his mind and how he sees the world. He gets me like that.

I bring him back to my place. We are in my room sitting on the edge of opposite sides of my bed like two polar molecules in a jar. He's been talking for a bit now, and I love it, but somewhere in our verbal exchange, the drama of Sigma Apple Pie is brought forth, leading to a convo about information I have to pretend I don't already know.

"My brother is actually in a different frat." Fuck. Time to act.

"Your brother?" I reply. I'm going to act like I have absolutely no idea that his brother or sister go and went to our school.

"Yeah, like my real brother is a senior, and he's graduating this year. My sister also went here."

He must know that I am a certified social media scavenger. He's just waiting for me to slip up. I know it.

"Oh wow, that's so cool. You must be so close with your family!" I keep it professional and on the awkward side. I think I passed the test. Shoutout to me for literally the best acting performance ever.

"Kind of—" He gets cut off midsentence by his phone vibration. "Sorry, I've got to take this."

He picks up his phone, and I can hear another girl crying on the other line. "Is it something with your parents? Is everything alright?" he asks her. He sounds so genuinely concerned and caring, and it is so attractive until the voice on the other line says, "Can you please come back?"

No. No. No. I have been absolutely obsessed with this boy and fantasizing about this moment for months. He is not leaving. He is staying right here with me. Forever. Just kidding (kind of). I'm not totally crazy, but now I think I kind of am.

"Sorry, there's this girl that became friends with the frat, and she's been having a lot of family issues. I think I might have to head back."

My rage ceases. I can't be upset. If he were to see me show negative emotion, it would greatly counteract the image he has of me. Aside from that, life happens, and if anything at all, I know he truly is a somewhat of a good person. Maybe now just isn't the best time, and the universe said "pause."

"Yeah, I totally understand. I can drive you back if you'd like."

"You're literally a saint. I can stay for a bit longer."

"Okay," I say as apathetically as possible.

"It's kind of wild. Like I think I have a way of attracting chaotic people into my life." We both pause. He seems afraid that I think he's a misogynist and I'm afraid that I am the exact chaos he's attracting.

"Not this girl, like, seriously nothing against her." He points to his phone in attempt to refute against the sexist undertone of his previous statement. "But when I was in high school, there was this girl who was about to—" He cut out and gestured towards his neck with his hands. I got what he was saying.

"But before she did, she called my house at, like, 2:00 a.m., saying that I was the only one who could save her." He opens his mouth as if he has more to say then closes it again to stop himself. "And yeah, there's been other stuff like that."

Considering how much I have viewed his location in the past ninety-six hours, he might actually be onto something. I think he inadvertently just called me the fuck out.

"Ah, interesting." I keep it short. If I didn't think he was right, I would definitely be put off. It gives off the same energy as people that feel the need to mention their ex is crazy. The ex is indeed *not* crazy 99.999999 percent of the time, and if they were in the slightest, the person saying they're crazy is often the one who made them crazy in the first place.

We head out. He seems so nervous to be in the car with me. He grabs the car handle on the roof like I'm about ready to run us into a tree.

"What kind of music do you like?" he asks me. He seems surprised to hear the faint sound of pop music coming from my speakers.

"Honestly just, like, pop and whatever is mainstream. How about you?"

"I really like electric. Like, electronica type of stuff." See, I knew he was "not like other guys" while simultaneously being exactly like other guys.

"Oh, cool," I say more enthusiastically and much less in a way that makes me sound as dry as a saltine cracker. I turn in to the semicircle that leads to the building.

"I hope I can see you again before I leave. I'm sorry it got cut short." He looks at me like he really means it. There's a deepness and sincerity in his voice. Before I can vigorously and consensually kiss him, he puts his disposable mask back on and disappears into the night. He'll be here for a few more days, yet not another Saturday night.

I don't know if I will ever see him again, but holy shit am I falling.

# CHAPTER 11

# HIGHWAY TO HELL (CHAD)

———

We never met up again during the remainder of Chad's time in St. Louis. He was too busy getting hammered with the boys, but after all, what else would Sundays, Mondays, and Tuesdays be for if not the boys? And his other side chicks, of course.

I still have a campaign to focus on, so I tell myself I don't even care. Maybe he didn't want to see me, and that's okay, but, like, I'd rather he tell me that I am the most annoying bitch alive and run me over with my own car than continue this little game. I just want the truth.

It's been about three weeks since that night, and we are now heading into the third week of July. About a week after he left, and two weeks before now, I told him that he should "come back to stl," to which he said, "Ofc, sometime before the end of summer." I internalized that, even though it was probably just something he thought he'd say to appease me, and it actually worked.

The idea of him sort of became the light at the end of a long day on the campaign—the fantasy that got me through hundreds of spreadsheets and thousands of columns. Analyzing trends among zip codes is more exciting with places to associate them with—places in which I can create my idealistic delusion of Chad and I's future.

The 63109 zip code has a coffee shop, which I have gone to on several occasions: a "once-reliable break service" turned hippie cafe with banana iced lattes and oat milk—a service for humanity a car shop could never attain. The owner is a bit of a badass: tattoo sleeves and a voice that would seem abrasive in New York City. Chad and I could never go there together, for it would disrupt the sweet romance of our affair.

The coffee shop in 63118 is much more peaceful. Wooden accents, bright red colors, and latte art. Its specialty is warm drinks in ceramic cups. Not the type of place I can drink three coffees in a two-hour duration staring at my computer and convincing myself I am being productive. The type of place where Ethiopian grounds brew meaningful conversation and laughter feels inappropriate in the sincerest way. I'd meet Chad at 63118 after receiving a full-time job offer in Los Angeles. Not directly after because directly after we'd be drinking lime margaritas—mine virgin, his with a dash of tequila—resting poolside beneath the sun, knowing many days like this are in my imminent future. A few days later, reality would set. Our physical distance would need to be discussed, and I would pick 63118.

The other people on the campaign are much cooler than I am, who fantasizes endlessly and can't form coherent sentences in the presence of groups of people. There are a few recent graduates from my school, each with their own unique vibe, relative to the rest of the world yet homogenously relative to each other—kind of everything I imagine when I think of the New York City vintage liberal aesthetic. Their clothes are secondhand yet mirror fast fashion trends. The type that wear black combat boots with long baggy jeans and a tight jacket during hundred-degree days in the St. Louis humidity that already feels like walking through a geyser filled with lava.

One of them is also from Minnesota. I can tell by her vocal undertones that she believes everything is either a hot dish or a salad—I am quite biased and pessimistic toward that state. It's a place where forced smiles cover up everything within, and nothing can ever escape aside from petty gossip. Not that she is anything like that. As I said, I'm biased.

Election day is three weeks away. Every time I hear the phrase "August the 4th," I come closer to completely losing it.

Baseball Jersey boy sits with his computer on his lap and his phone in his hand. I turn to face the back of his head, sending only strong negative vibrations his way. He better not fucking say it.

"Can I count on your vote August the 4th?"

FUCK. He said it.

The tension that was already the equivalent of a one-meter cord being stretched from Mississippi to Oklahoma is somehow increasing. Every phone call feels like a life-or-death situation. The weight of every St. Louis quality-of-life metric is on my shoulders with each and every phone call.

The office is quiet today. The postgrads are huddled on the couch, typing away and making calls. The phone at the front of the office rings. Adrastos answers. He puts down the phone and calls for a team meeting.

"We need to get out," he says, completely deadpan. We evacuate the building, and Adrastos walks me to my car.

To be in America is to fear getting shot for trying to get people access to health care. Some people would rather kill than live in a world where everyone has the basic necessities to live.

Adrastos sends me some spreadsheets to work on remotely. The most extroverted people complain about the forced arrangement, especially since we'd just been freed from the tightest COVID restrictions, but the quieter ones don't seem to mind. And in spite of the broader seriousness of this issue, I can use this remote work as an opportunity. I don't have to be in St. Louis to work on spreadsheets.

Is this my main character origin story?

Working on the campaign is my stability amid this void, and that has proven to not be so stable. The static numbers in rows and columns are a misfit in continually evolving conditions.

Maybe, I was made for chaos. The universe needed someone to be incredibly pretty and intelligent to possess the sum awkwardness from an entire country's first day of puberty. I am a small chunk of complete static indeterminacy needed to keep the world balanced.

What's the most spontaneous thing I can do?

Sitting at my computer and asking myself this question is giving me deja vu. No research this time. That's not spontaneous.

Who's the one person I want to see right now?

I think you already know the answer to that.

He's seventeen hours away from me but I must go. Airlines are practically begging people to fly again, so I could probably buy a cheap plane ticket, but since I am choosing to travel among the pandemic, I should err on the side of caution and drive.

I shovel clothes into my backpack and throw blankets in the backseat of my car.

I should probably tell him I'm coming, but I need to keep it low-key because this could easily be read as "I am so crazy and obsessive that I drove over two thousand miles for you," which I don't think is true. I don't know why I do things or why he is the answer to my life's satisfaction. I don't know why I view him the way I do, and I don't truly know how I view him at all. In a world where nothing actually matters, he is one of the few things that does. And I know it makes no sense, and it isn't even a positive aspect, but there's something about him that makes me obsessed.

I draft a text in my notes app, examining it a few times before typing it out in the messaging app.

> "but what if I came to New York
> like soonish?"

It's the perfect rebuttal to our conversation weeks prior where I told him to come to St. Louis, but it almost seems so chill that it's trying too hard. Fuck it. I retype it and hit send.

I insert myself in the car and drive before he can even reply. Nothing is going to change my mind. This is my destiny.

As an eighteen-year-old, I have yet to do something that is deemed an incredibly poor decision. I was always too busy being a #girlboss in high school that I never had the time or energy to be any form of a rebellious teen. I mean, driving to Chicago for some rando that DMed me on Instagram at the apex of uncertainty wasn't necessarily a smart decision, but I wouldn't consider it anything like this.

I've also never drank even a singular sip of alcohol. I've never done any illicit substance for that matter.

I've never done anything that I can look back on later and think, "Wow, that was really stupid," and I want to have one of those experiences so that others can live vicariously through me while having the gift of being much smarter than I, so this is it. There aren't too many serious repercussions aside from the potential of others thinking I am absolutely batshit out of my mind, which is a pretty fair assessment. And I totally do care about what others think of me, but like usual, I'm going to pretend like I do not.

My consciousness has sort of shut off. Driving has become an unconscious action, and my deep, philosophical thoughts are not with me. A mystical mirage of yellow and red blurs the near-distant horizon. Love's gas station. A little stick on the dash at fifteen degrees. Gas.

It's slightly past 2:00 a.m., so I've been driving for a few hours. I should see what Chad said. I'd honestly be surprised if he isn't still awake, given that he gets up at like 5:00 p.m.

"omg come to Westchester, we can
meet up"

That seems like the type of message that is one's innate response as an act of courtesy. Yes, it's nice and if he meant it, it's good. Yet I don't think he really knows how literally I meant it when I mentioned coming to New York "soonish."

"cool, I'm omw"

He's probably still going to think I'm being sarcastic.

"Wait actually?"

He replies almost immediately. I knew he was awake and wouldn't believe it.

"spontaneity is litty"

I strategically use the word "litty" to cater to my audience of one. It is cringe in any other context, and a little cringe in this one. I have never said I am cool.

"lmao, that's crazy"

Yeah, he's kind of right. Not going to argue either this or I are not crazy.

Before I can reply, he sends another message: "Keep me posted!" Wow, he used an exclamation mark and everything. He's probably just enthusiastic because he's been on a three-week dry spell because his family just moved to New York, and he doesn't know any other people he can fuck. None-theless, I persist, back onto the freeway and away from my consciousness.

It's been some amount of time between ten and sixty minutes, but I'm currently not shrewd enough to know. I know it's legal to sleep in the back seat of my car at rest stops and Walmart parking lots. That sounds nice.

I pull into a rest stop and turn the car off. I meander into the backseat and throw my black-and-white floral blanket over my face and body as a form of protection. I set a timer on my phone for three and a half hours.

\*\*\*

The summery sun wakes me with its radiant photons. The blanket over my entire body has created a greenhouse effect, leaving my skin covered in sticky sweat. Did the AC shut off?

I peak through an opening and my body jolts back as though I've been struck by pure electricity. Instead of seeing bedroom wall, I only see truck. Where am I? Why the fuck am I in the backseat of a car? The truck's driver opens the driver's side door, ready to "skrt." Am I at a rest stop?

I reach for my phone, and it all comes back to me. Another unread message from Chad from Sigma Apple Pie sticks out in the middle of my screen: "lol this is actually crazy"

I feel like he's trying to keep the communication going, so I shall. I send a pic of the rest stop with the caption: "Just woke up." I add a sticker so he knows this is Indiana. It'll be the first thing he sees when he wakes up, like, twelve hours from now.

I put my mask on and make my way inside to grab a snack. The vegan-ness in me leaves for a sec as I insert my crumbly dollar into a slim slit to purchase a bag of cheddar crackers, making sure to sanitize my hands vigorously before and after so COVID does not have the slightest chance to get to me. The cheesy crunch powder kind of deserves the hype to be honest. Each square in the bag reminds me of when Chad decided to bleach his hair about three weeks into the pandemic. He didn't realize that he was supposed to add toner, and the color turned out the exact shade as the stale greasy cheese crackers in my palm.

I finish the bag and throw it into the trash can. I take a good look at Indiana, which is a paradox in itself. Is there really such a thing as a "good look" in the state of Indiana? That's definitely an uninformed and biased take, but as a Midwesterner, I feel entitled to make it. To New York I shall go.

Twenty miles out from the rest stop, and I have a freshly made venti iced caramel cloud macchiato with almond milk. Everything can change—milage, feelings, the guy I'm driving across the country to see—but not macchiatos. They are a constant in my life.

Unlike the painstaking trek through rural Illinois with only the abundance of Culver's as a visual reliever, the biggest hurdle in my journey to the East Coast is Ohio. It's incredibly long, and nothing feels authentic. Whether it's cornfields or moderately sized industrialization, something about this state feels disingenuous.

My tentative destination comes to mind, causing my grip on the steering wheel to loosen as I break out into a thick sweat. This is low-key so embarrassing. I can't even think about *him* without becoming a smelly ice cube, radiating heat as I melt. It's even more embarrassing that *him* is Chad from Sigma Apple Pie, who probably just wants to fuck and forget my name immediately after. I increase the decibels of my Taylor Swift CD as my form of woman empowerment.

I keep driving. I won't let myself stop till I get to a major city in Ohio like Columbus so I can send a photo to my friends with a digital Ohio sticker, and they'll be so confused and intrigued and give me my earned attention. I'll probably add some sort of nonchalant caption like, "When you decide that Chad from Sigma Apple Pie is your destiny so you drive to NY," and they'll be like, "Omg, Olivia, you're so silly." I'll be satisfied with myself, knowing people think I am interesting.

Major cities also have an oversaturated Starbucks market, so I can get a pink drink to make my selfie look even cooler.

"The question is not what you look at, but what you see." Henry David Thoreau might have been onto something.

It's all variations of the concrete jungle or clamorous vacancy, but never the antithesis of either. Eighty-mile-an-hour freeways permeated with constant traffic kiss the surrounding areas that claim to be absent of population density like a cringey high school band couple. Neighborhoods with more people than occupied housing units have their forms of gluttonous isolation. Everywhere has its green. Flourishing green creates faded green for "captains of industry"; it's all part of the same withering system. The trees are nothing unfamiliar. The imagery evoked from person to person at the mention of green trees on the side of the freeway is standard. The green from the trees goes into my hands and to the gasoline merchant, only to go back to the trees as a toxic, tangible brown.

Nonetheless, I am no less of a gluttonous beast as the rest as I hand my payment to the merchant for a grande pink drink. I stop the car in the parking lot, which is where I will sit until I know people think I am cool. I execute the aforementioned selfie plan and my friends are "literally dead." Submission complete.

Chad asked me how the drive was going and once again I am reminded how crazy this is. I respect his opinion. Who am I to say this isn't crazy?

"It's going well, I think I'm like
seven hours away"

I should probably figure out where I'm staying tonight. I read a play once titled *Lost in Yonkers*, and I think it would be clever if I found a place there. Based on the fictional story I read, it doesn't seem like *city* city, but it seems quite close to the real city.

There is one place in Yonkers for under fifty dollars. The outside looks like a little cottage with a brown-and-white blend of stone and brick. There's a bright red door and intense purple flowers that differentiate themselves from the greenery. The inside looks. . . okay. If it were a hotel, it'd be the type of place where a Karen would slap the person at the front desk after taking a step inside.

I don't mind, though. It seems alright; the location is good. I can immerse myself in a Pulitzer Prize winner. A win all around.

I think I'm getting geographically closeish. I'm in Pennsylvania, and I found a radio station with some authentic jazz music, which feels like NYC to me.

The sky is pitch black, but I don't think this road has ever been pitch black with the high volume of traffic and soft white headlights. I see my first sign for New York City, but based on the disregard for any safety in the drivers around me, I could've guessed I was getting increasingly close.

The number of cars decreases as each exit passes. Now it's all trucks. Any wrong movement, and my life is over. If I fatally collided with a truck, the millions of people in the city would not even see me as a life. I am so small. There is no reason I need to inflict such judgement and stress on myself. No one cares in this city of high-rises and penthouses of the most wealthy, elite, intellectual, creative, and successful people.

I am only as big as I let myself feel. My stressors and anxiety are only as large as I perceive them.

I arrive to my place in Yonkers. It's time to rest.

## CHAPTER 12

# BATHTUB ACTORS

---

I wake up on a rock with a napkin-thin sheet that someone had the audacity to call a bed. I pull up my finsta post from last night, which was a silly little photo of myself with pursed lips and the caption "I may have just impulsively hopped in the car last night and drove over one thousand miles (to NY) for Chad from Sigma Apple Pie #oops." I scroll through the comments.

"This is so inspiring but also you good?" I mean I think I'm good, but who's to say.

"Truly iconic dick appointment. An inspiration." Haha, true.

"You're an inspiration" Lmao.

"HUH??" I forget that people who only knew me in high school think I'm some well-organized and mentally stable type-A person.

"Girl I . . . don't even know what to say" Fair.

The general consensus is that I'm cool, and even though no one said it, I'm a bit of a clout chaser. I didn't do this for clout, but I'm definitely going to capitalize off of it for clout.

Chad told me he's never been to Yonkers, and I can't help but wonder if he's also read *Lost in Yonkers*. He probably read it much differently than me because I can't imagine he has any relatives that don't absolutely adore him. He has his way with people, and his charisma seems especially appealing in a family setting. His Scorpio Mars and Pisces Venus are too intuitive, kind, and empathetic.

I decide to take a walk outside. The streets are crowded; it's a dense suburbia. I can see the megacity in the distance. Nothing feels real.

I look down to see one missed call from "Mother." She has no idea. The last time we spoke was two days ago when I was in St. Louis. Mother's eighteen-year-old daughter who had never gone so far as to drink a singular sip of alcohol has just driven over one thousand miles for a frat bro. She's not going to believe it.

I call her back. I'm going to scan her vibe before I say anything.

"Hey, mom." I try to avoid overenthusiasm because that would be suspicious.

"Hi, honey! What are you up to?" She seems to be in a happy mood.

"Nothing much, just going for a walk." That technically wasn't a lie.

"What do you got going on today?" I can't tell what the intentions behind that question are.

"Nothing much. Just campaign stuff." Still not a lie.

"Okay, well, just thought I'd call and say hi."

The conversation ends, and honestly, I don't know how I would've mentioned that I was in New York. It wasn't something that could've easily been slipped into the conversation, so I feel less bad about being a terrible child. Honestly, what good would come out of telling her? She has an anxious outlook on the world and knowing her daughter is in New

York would only make her more anxious, so by not telling her, I'm preventing her from getting anxious in the first place. I'm actually doing a good thing.

I'll tell her eventually. Maybe I'll wait until, like, five years from now when I'm a perceptually more mature person, and we can laugh at it together.

My intern manager sends me another array of unorganized spreadsheets that need to be worked on. There's a lot of analysis and strategy that goes into campaigns, especially given the severe cost constraint of a grassroots campaign.

I'm moving locations for the night. My place in Yonkers does not allow guests and not that I even think Chad would even want to come over in the first place, but I want to be prepared anyway. I find a place about forty-five minutes north in a city called Nyack. I think playwright Jason Robert Brown lived there, and he worked at a local theater when he was fifteen. Another sign from the universe to move locations.

I told the owners of my room for the night that another person was spending the night, just to be safe. I can't check in until 3:00 p.m., and in the completely off chance Chad wants to come over, he probably won't want to until at least 10:00 p.m.—he's predictable like that.

Nyack is a cute town that feels small despite being very population dense. The roads are narrow, steep, and packed with cars, and the architecture feels homely rather than industrial. There's a nameless used bookstore, and I must go in. I purchase a book as a keepsake because it's something I can keep forever to remember this voyage without ever getting questioned about it. It'll be my own secret in broad daylight. *Power Politics* by Arundhati Roy will forever be with me.

The smoothie shop next door is filming a promo video, so I must go in. I confidently strut my way to the counter: practice for my future modeling career after this promo video for some smoothie shop goes viral. Chad's family will see the video and be like, "OMG this girl is so pretty and smart!" and Chad will have to sit there and listen to them talk about my greatness. I purse my lips around the straw of my raspberry blast smoothie. I am so seductive, it's unreal.

I pace back and forth on the steep streets of Nyack, alternating between looking at houses stacked on houses and sailboats on the water. The crosswalks are misleading here because most of the drivers do not stop even if there's a stop sign.

"Hey, be more fucking careful!" A driver reels down the passenger window to yell at me as I put one foot on the crosswalk. I guess I'll stay on the sidewalk for now. My phone lights up with a message from Chad.

"What do you want to do?"

I have such an endless list of things that I want to do with Chad that I don't even know where to start.

"You're the leading NY
expert soooo"

I'm getting smoother.

"hey, I've only lived here for less
than a year"

He deflects it back to me.

> "Do you want to hang out where
> I'm staying?"

"yeah, send me the addy"

Once again, seems like he's interested in me, but he also just moved here after living somewhere else his whole life, so he's probably been bored out of his mind and just desperate to see someone the slightest bit familiar.

"Wow, you're kinda far, like forty-
five minutes away"

Shit.

"I'm still down though, dw"

Bless. Wait, he's actually willing to drive a ninety-minute round trip for me? No, never mind. He's probably just bored.

> "I think I'll be free around 8"

That gives me about five hours to work on the campaign.

"Yeah, that works, I'm probably
going to work out"

Why did he feel the need to tell me that?

When 3:00 p.m. rolls around, I make my way up the streets to the apex of the hills to check into my room. I walk to the front door and am greeted by a woman who looks too perfect for reality. If I had to take a guess, I'd say she's sixty, but she looks absolutely flawless. The way her curly red hair compliments her light blue eyes subtracts thirty years from her visual age. The man in this house shows his age much more directly. His scalp is bald, yet he has an icy gray beard he must have spent the last fifty-eight years growing *at least*. He has a leather jacket and a stoic presence, a biker without a bike. They don't look like two people that would be married or in a relationship, and maybe they aren't, but they are two people that are in this house. I know that much to be true.

"Welcome in, I'm Nadja! Where's your friend?" This is going to be an awkward conversation.

"Oh, he's coming later. He lives in New York, and he's just going to visit later." Is she really just going to sit and watch some guy come over later, hang out in my room for a bit, and leave? That's literally so awkward, which I guess is on brand for me.

"We were just filming. We are working on a series where we tell tales from the bathtub. We think it's kind of fitting for the times."

That somehow makes so much sense to me. Nadja shows me two separate bathrooms placed right next to each other.

"The one on the right is where we are filming, and the one on the left is the one you can use."

Makes so much sense. Of course, bathtub actors forty minutes outside of New York City would need two bathrooms right next to each other. That's such a niche issue, and I'm glad to know there's a solution.

I walk into my room. The room is coated with primary colors and a light brown wooden floor. In between the parted yellow curtains with light blue bows is a view that screams the tropics. The clouds are inches above the horizon. There are hidden pops of other colors from the rainbow amid the green. It's like the view from the top of a mountain with a purely tropical terrain. The endless array of greenery is a view I thought only $5,000 performative altruism service trips could buy. The trees look so different from above; they're so luscious. It's like I'm standing above a bin of broccoli at a grocery store.

On the red bookshelf to the right of me there is a collection of theatrical and culinary literature. *More Golden Rules of Acting: that nobody ever tells you* sticks out like a sore thumb. The owner of this house is probably another aspiring actress with an abundance of doubts in herself who continues to get closer and closer to chasing her dreams because nothing is ever actually new, and similarly, the culinary literature is no different. Inches from Nyman's work is an array of culinary books, each with a neutral background color and a main dish highlighted in the center. *Half Baked Harvest Super Simple*, *Jubilee*, and *Jerusalem: A Cookbook* all feature unique variations on the same foundations: tomatoes, a neutral-colored sauce, and a nonmammal-based protein. Every book on this shelf seems like a variation of another, to some degree.

There is noise coming from the outside of the white door to the left of me. It must be Nadja filming content for her upcoming web series. I sit on the bed with my back against the light blue wall in an abyss of loud primary colors. I take a deep breath in.

Wow.

Thirty-nine hours ago, I asked myself who the one person I wanted to see was, and it brought me here. My impulsivity brought me one thousand miles away from the rural Midwest to the rural East Coast—to seeing trees from below to seeing trees from above. I am in this upper middle-class cottage-style home with a guest bedroom. I get to work.

***

I get a text.

"omw"

He's on his way!

I untie the bows and close the yellow curtains to hide my appearance from the driveway. He doesn't need to see me pacing back and forth, knowing that my end is near. He doesn't need to see me rush to my computer to open different software development apps to make myself seem cool, smart, and mysterious. He either rejects me now or we continue on with our heads in the clouds till the helicopter of reality departs us. Maybe that's pessimistic, but the only thing that can come from this is an ending.

Maybe, we continue on as some sort of in-between, but even still an ending will come. I think am in love, and I want so badly for it to be us for now. If even for a moment it could be us, that would be enough. For now.

The little cracks between the curtains reveal a midnight sky until they are filled by a flash of LED light. He is here. I swing open the white door to my bedroom, then tentatively unlock the red front door. I step outside to greet him. He is so much taller than I remember. He must be at least a foot taller than me, wearing gray sweatpants and a white T-shirt—I told you he was predictable. My foot rotates as I walk, and I almost fall over on the freshly mowed grass. This doesn't feel real.

We walk in together and he waves to the bearded man and Nadja like a sixteen-year-old trying to get a father's approval to ask his daughter to the prom. They totally know we are about to fuck right now. So awk.

He closes the door behind him. I sit on the short edge of the bed; he sits on the long. This positioning is even more awkward than the last. There has to be more than six feet between us—how appropriate nowadays. The CDC would be so proud of us.

"Sooo, what do your parents think of this?" He breaks the ice. Shit, I still haven't told my mother.

"I actually haven't told them yet." I smile as his eyes widen. "Do you have any suggestions on how I should go about that?"

He breaks out into slight laugher, somewhere between a pity laugh and a genuine laugh. We both pause.

I heard that you can see someone's life story in their eyes, and maybe that's why he's always looking in mine. In his, I see a monotonous shade, perhaps symbolic of a future 9-to-5 that he absolutely hates. Perhaps he undermines his talent and convinces himself that corporate America is the only way to his own demise.

But maybe I'm just projecting.

"How's the campaign going?"

That was a loaded question.

"Good!" I'm such a liar, and I just described a verb with an adjective. I can't believe I said "good" instead of "well." "It's definitely getting more tense."

"I'm sure you've got this." No, Chad. You think I'm a perfectionist that never loses anything, so your opinion isn't relevant. Yeah, it was definitely getting more tense.

"What have you been up to?" I ask.

"Honestly, reading a lot. I've been reading a lot of international literature, and I started volunteering at the suicide hotline."

Wow. Maybe, I try too hard to convince myself he's heartless. Maybe it's easier that way. Maybe it's easier to get rejected by someone who lacks compassion and empathy.

We keep talking, and he tells me more about the drama in Sigma Apple. I mean I figured it was only a matter of time, and I have been on the edge of my seat since he brought it up last time.

"Do you want to watch a movie?"

Wait. What? Chad? I freeze. He probably thinks I didn't hear him as I stare at his lips trying to comprehend if I'm going insane and hearing voices in my head, or if he actually said that.

"Yeah. Sure." Nice, Olivia. Way to be cool. You are so calm and collected.

I grab my computer from the floor off the right side of the bed. All the hard work I did in opening the geekiest of applications is about to pay off. Don't mind the terminal, I was just working on creating a virtual environment. It's really no big deal.

"You pick," I hand him the computer as we sit on the bed, still inches apart from each other in the dark.

"I have to pick? Okay, um. How do you feel about this?" The mouse hovers over the Mark Zuckerberg fictional documentary.

"Yeah, that's good."

He brings his arm around me and pulls me close like two tectonic plates colliding and merging to form something greater than its counterparts.

IT'S HAPPENING. IT'S HAPPENING. IT'S HAPPENING.

This whole fucking time, I knew it. I wasn't lying to myself. I wasn't going crazy. He genuinely does like me back, and this whole time it's been mutual. In spite of all my painfully awkward mannerisms and bodily failures that happen whenever he's around, he really does like me, and I deserve this. I am so much more than I see myself, and he sees it in me even though I never do. He sees how hard I work and how much I try and that despite all of the wrongful things I do, I genuinely want to make this world right.

I move my left hand to his right shoulder while my head clings to his chest. I'm trying to gather myself and process what's going on. This is everything I think I've ever wanted. You know that trope in every coming-of-age movie ever, when the character we are told to think is nerdy and unattractive gets with their lifelong crush that we are told to think is super popular and unattainable, but it works out anyway? Well, this was that, except so much more.

When I was in high school, I got rejected four times during Sadie Hawkins season, two of which were pure public humiliation. I folded the crispy edges of a large poster board as my hands shook at the end of a basketball game in a stadium filled with hundreds of people, maybe over a thousand. "I'll have to think about it." He walked away as I stood holding up the poster for the large crowd of people to see, only to later find out the proposal was a well-executed setup by a group of boys who wanted to humiliate me.

Why am I so unlovable? Why am I never enough?

I really try to be a good person, and I know sometimes, or actually all of the time, my face turns bright red when I speak to someone unfamiliar. And I know I never have the right things to say, and I know sometimes I make mistakes.

My father always told me the worst thing I could ever be is a woman. I was taught women were crazy and emotional, and I was never to be one. I was to be quiet and determined, nothing more. When I did things that went against that, I was to be ignored for weeks. I developed a stutter in my speech when I was a young teen because I was so afraid to speak to him. "Things used to be so good until you ruined everything," he would often say.

Variations of that circulated constantly, and I knew I was such a failure. When I was younger, he took me to California because he knew how much I wanted to be an actress and we went to Universal Studios and ate sushi. He seemed happy to be a father, and that made me happy. We stayed in Burbank and saw street performers and went to Venice Beach, and I ruined everything by aging.

For my seventeenth birthday he gave me the words I had known to be true for quite some time, but for the first time ever he said them blatantly and too clear to ignore: "I don't care about you. What do you expect?" he said straight to my face in the early afternoon after I asked him if he wanted to do something for my birthday. A few days prior, when I walked in on him playing video games for forty-eight hours straight with a whole case of liquor in his system, he mentioned California, and he didn't just reminisce the good times, but he said that we could have even better times if we returned. Somewhere beneath him is a person, and I just want to be good enough.

I got a cell phone when I was eight and an email address at the same age. I think my mom was scared. Sometimes I look back at the emails I sent him. I remember when he had high blood pressure so I searched the web for every low sodium option I could possibly find and compiled it into an email. I just wanted him to stop telling me how much he wanted to die. Was I not enough to want to live? I want you to live, Daddy, I—

"Daddy, I just want to talk to you. Can you please let me in?" After I had won an award and failed to give him proper recognition, I wasn't allowed in his house for over a month. He had sent me an email threatening to completely detach, which wasn't necessarily new, but I just wanted to talk to him. He had his phone inches from my face, seconds after I showed up to the door. "Subject is clearly irrational and threatening," were his only words to me as he recorded my every move—if rocking back and forth unable to even walk from emotional distress could be considered a move—and tears streamed down my face wondering why he wouldn't let me in his home. Was I really that disgusting and horrible and unlovable?

"I'm just trying to talk to my dad. I just want to—I just want to—" I began to malfunction and repeat myself over and over, never to break my focus on the camera in case someone was to see it and see my cry for help. Maybe they would know that I really try to be a good person, and in spite of my flaws, maybe I am.

I'm trying to keep it together as I rest my head on Chad's heartbeat. I'm shaking, but his heart is racing. The anxiety is mutual. I push myself away from his chest and look at him. His hair was the same shade of orange as the stale bag of cheese crackers from the Midwestern rest stop, and I have never so badly wanted my fingers to be covered in an orange film that not even the universal solvent could dissolve.

I comb my fingers through the back of his hair, and he pulls me in. We kiss. And we are kissing some more, and this is everything I've wanted, and I never want it to end. All the cumulative bad in my life is being sucked out of me, and everything was worth it.

We kiss more and more until we stop and hold each other in a lasting embrace. He lifts his wrist above me to look at his watch.

"I have to go." I think he can sense my internal remorse as he said that. "I lied about where I was going, and my parents expect me back by one."

I move myself off him and we both get up off the bed. We stand together in front of the door, and he pulls me in again to kiss me. He pulls away and I grab his wrist as he turns toward the door.

He looks down on me and laughs, his expression asking, "What?"

I have to say what's on my mind, or I'll forever regret it.

"I'm, like, actually into you. Like, this was more than just a 'hookup' to me." I keep my eyes pointed at the ground until after I am finished speaking. We hang in silence for a bit until I look up at him, trying to hide the tears I could feel coming.

"I'm not looking for a relationship." I nod and look back down at the floor.

"I expected that." I smile slightly because what did I really expect? He couldn't escape his long ancestry of college sophomores.

"I like hanging out with you though."

"Yeah."

He turns away and heads off into the night. The LEDs reappear in the cracks between the yellow curtains, turning up the hill and taking away the light at the end of the tunnel. And for the first time in a really long time, I cry.

# CHAPTER 13

# TEENAGE REALIZATION MOMENT

———

I wake up with a sticky face from a mass conglomeration of messy tears and an overwhelming emptiness. Everything I ever wanted came true until it didn't, leaving me without the fantasy that I had so consistently held onto, and calling it a fantasy is optimistic, because in reality, I really did devote myself to a delusion. My brain manipulated interactions between us to create a reality that was never really there, and now I am left alone in an increasingly isolating pandemic world, no one to latch on to and no way to escape.

I messaged him last night after he left because I have a tendency to dig my own grave.

> "just to be clear, I didn't drive to
> NY for you"

I send it in a desperate attempt to maintain my postmodern coolness. I wish I could time travel ten hours back and yell at myself to "stfu."

"I genuinely really do like you, but
you are not the driving force in
my life"

Who the fuck says this? To Olivia from ten hours ago: TAKE THE L AND MOVE ON. It's a bit difficult to make him think I have no emotions and was just bored when Olivia from ten hours ago is an antagonistic dweeb.

I pull up his sister's social media to further envision Chad, and in attempt to hold onto everything that was before it became everything that isn't now. She has a new post from this morning. It's a candid selfie of her and Chad, somewhere in the streets of New York with the caption "I love my brother"

I stare at the screen for quite some time.

The thought of loving Chad, a thought that had previously felt so right, now feels distant.

I don't think I know what love really is, or if this thorough delusion I created could even be considered love, but I know that I wanted it to be Chad and I. And it *was*. . . for an instance. And emptiness is weighty.

I get out of bed and walk into the living room. Nadja and the bearded man are sitting at the dining room table sipping on hot tea.

"Where'd your friend go?" Nadja asks as she looks into my room.

I haven't the slightest clue how to answer that. Any form of truth requires a longer explanation, and even if she takes the hint, she'll think I was played, and I don't want anyone to think Chad is a bad person for this because I really just played myself. It was I who developed an unhealthy obsession with Chad and let it drive me to my own internal demise. This isn't his wrongdoing, it's mine.

"Oh, he went home." I smile and speak as though I'm revealing positive news, but her facial expression softens, and I can tell she thinks I'm hurting. I am, but she doesn't need to know that.

I wonder if this is the type of thing she talks about with her friends. When her friends are like, "Nadja, what's renting out your home like?" She's probably like "Oh, I recently had some teenager come over just to hook up with some random guy while I filmed for my bathtub series. She drove like one thousand miles to get here too." And they probably all laugh about what it's like to be a teen and then they feel some sympathy for my heartbreak.

I can't stop thinking about that one night when Chad told me he has a history of attracting crazy into his life. After this, I now consider myself his definition of crazy, and I wonder why I was so mesmerized by him. Maybe it's his apathetic vibe. The way he conceals his emotions makes me feel at peace. Knowing that all of my chaos, even in its most unstable state, could be absorbed by his neutral and static disposition is calming.

This was a risk; I knew that coming in. I cannot change the outcome, but I can take this moment for all it is and accept it with all its pain.

The East Coast is a reminder of my insignificance in this world. There are millions of people smarter and better than me in every regard, millions of people I will never know and millions of people I will never even care to. Millions of people who will never care to know me all condensed into one area the size of a thumb on a paper map.

And that's comforting. Knowing that all the stress and anxiety I place on myself is entirely arbitrary in the grand scheme of life is a thought I have yet to fully come to terms with. The fear of others' perception locks me into isolation, yet I've never stopped to realize everyone is too self-absorbed to actually care. In a region with bottomless brunch and million-dollar bonuses and more distractions than there is even attention to be distracted by, no one cares about some stranger they pass by on their way to get a bagel after their 3:00 a.m. sneaky link in Murray Hill. And despite the exaggeration of insignificance on the East Coast, it's really no different anywhere else.

People in my Midwestern college dining hall—the one which I would actively avoid by ordering ahead then quickly picking up my food and eating alone in my room because the thought of being seen was too overwhelming—are the exact same. Everyone is too worried about their own successes while battling their own inferiorities that eat at them like leprosy from the inside out to ever even notice me.

Being on the East Coast, and forty-five minutes north of "The City" in a smaller city that is still so visibly crowded, brings that feeling to fruition, and I am thankful Chad gave me this perspective. Of all the people in all of existence, I can't help but wonder why Chad and I collided in this physical dimension of time and space.

I wonder what I brought to his life. Sure, I did all his homework for him and gave him one good time, but I refuse to believe that is all. There has to be something else from our interaction that he gained.

But maybe it's really not that deep to him like it is to me. Perhaps I taught him that people are more complex than they seem. He saw me as the organized and sophisticated professional from the start yet slowly began to watch his expectations of me twist and break. I could be his warning reference for some future encounter to come.

I envision him meeting someone, a potential roommate perhaps. They meet a vintage café. Chad arrives five minutes late, which is early for him, to see his potential roommate already sipping a hot cup of plain black coffee and wearing black jeans and a navy T-shirt. It's not reinventing the wheel, but it's not as basic as blue jeans and a white T-shirt.

They begin to talk about their lives. Potential Roommate has a standard 9-to-5. He doesn't particularly love it, but it's part of his greater plan, and people that love their 9-to-5 are a capitalist myth, so it isn't unordinary and it's enough to infer that he is ambitious. He grew up in a suburb of Chicago, nothing too exciting, but not entirely monotonous either. He comes from a nuclear family with the standard size of four and parents that are semi-happily together but there are certainly nights where his dad sleeps on the coach because of his "snoring."

Chad continues the familial discussion by talking a bit about his expanded nuclear family of five and growing up in Los Angeles, which is objectively cooler than a suburb of Chicago, as Potential Roommate points out. His comment breaks the ice and they talk some more, keeping it casual yet professional, and the more they talk, Chad can sense that Potential Roommate is intentionally evasive, avoiding questions like "Do you have any hobbies?" with a simple, "Haha, not really," as he frantically grabs his cup of coffee off the table. It appears there's so much on his mind with the incorrect words to match, scrambled stories with no clear arc. Potential Roommate is anxious in a way that Chad hasn't seen since college, in a way that he would much rather avoid.

Chad brings his cup of coffee to the trash can as a way of catalyzing their meeting's end. He says his goodbyes and begins to search for someone new, and just hours later, he is navigating through different applications for roommate inquiries while sitting front row to the local news channel on a living room TV. The anchorman discusses the weather, nothing too exciting. Chad reaches for the remote until a photo of Potential Roommate flashes on the screen followed by video footage of his arrest just blocks from the coffee shop.

Potential Roommate was poaching exotic snakes as a side hustle, and if they would have lived together, Chad could have been charged for assisting the snake poacher. If Chad hadn't hit on some mediocre-looking girl that did all his homework for him, he wouldn't have been able to recognize the signs of an undercurrent of chaos hidden beneath a desperately polished veneer of structure and zeal and could've spent the rest of his life behind bars.

That's my theory—for now. Time will tell. One day, when he reaches out years later during his temporary decline while I am simultaneously thriving, this madness will all make sense.

And even if this really is the end, and even though my eighteen-year-old ego is destroyed knowing I could be so insignificant to someone who was so significant to me, he got me through the past few months, and for that I am forever grateful. The thought of him got me out of bed and ready for online learning, inhibiting my recession into a dark depression I had come to know too well.

If a generic frat boy who doesn't care about me is the reason I was able to see another day, then I'm thankful that the universe sent him my way.

While I may be heartbroken, the campaign is more important than my feelings, so I must return, both to St.

Louis and to actual reality, which is currently rising COVID cases and increasingly rising inequity in a world that's already so structurally unjust.

Foot on the gas, I have a fifty-two-year political dynasty to defeat.

# CHAPTER 14

# #W

———

My first day back in the office is mostly comprised of phone calls, and so far, they've gone one of two ways.

I start with, "Hi, how are you?" To which they reply with an innocent, "Hello, I'm good" in the type of neutral tone that you wouldn't expect to betray you, comparable to a kind teacher or a friendly acquaintance. Not a super deep connection, but more positive than negative.

"I'm calling with Cori Bush for Congress. Can we count on your vote for August the 4th?"

Then there's a slight pause during which the other person on the line can fully gather their rage. It's almost like they've been observing the general public and taking notes for the past four weeks, waiting for this moment to unleash a thorough list of things they think the campaign has lied about, which are never actually things the campaign has lied about—they are just lies that have been said by the general public to try to help the opponent.

Or, after their slight pause, they proceed to berate me personally as though I am not an incredibly fragile eighteen-year-old girl who quite literally hides from her fear of being perceived and am instead someone who was so conniving and bored that she decided to orchestrate an elaborate scheme to pester and annoy the one, singular person on the other end of the line.

I will admit some of the lies are creative, and as a writer, I feel a certain moral obligation to not repeat them because I know how often information gets taken out of context, and so to maintain professionalism, all I will say is the opponent must be hella desperate if they are willing to go to such lengths.

Adrastos and I have not spoken since I've returned. A part of me thinks we are both too stressed for words, yet another part of me wonders if I am not alone in my own tendency to randomly convince myself that everyone hates me. Regardless, I receive my tasks from others in the office, or he'll send me some spreadsheets via email, and I really just help wherever I can.

So much of the campaign is being done manually; there are stacks of hand-written postcards and letters with spreadsheets full of manually entered addresses. If tech was integrated into the campaign, our purchasing power would drastically increase, and maybe more grassroots campaigns could easily compete against multi-billion-dollar corporations, and perhaps the people could finally have a decent fraction of the power that "democracy" suggests they have, but that's just a thought.

As of now, the biggest threat is voter suppression—both for mail and in person. As I was compiling a how-to guide for mail-in voters, I found myself nervously sweating, ultimately deciding I would vote in-person because I was so relentlessly confused by all the rules. One wrong pencil movement and a vote could be completely scratched, all the painstaking work attempting to reach one particular voter completely thrown away by a dull layer of lead. And while I am privileged to be able to vote in person, it appears other people may not have that same privilege, as rumors of closing polling locations circulate, and I can hear phone conversations attempting to pry election officials for more information.

This is yet another form of the "power of the people" illusion, because "the people"—who are in great part the working class who may not have stable access to transportation—no longer have a reliable polling location to cast their vote, leaving their fate in the hands of a few elites who don't care about them.

I digress.

The most important day is August 4th, which is Election Day, the Missouri primary elections, of course. As many people go to the polls undecided, in-person support on that day is crucial. I've been tasked with volunteer optimization, and my inner child who lives for academic validation and geeking out is thriving. There is a lot of data and a lot of ways I could approach this problem, but with the end goal being optimization, some ways could be significantly better than others.

I decide to start with the 2018 election data, then compare it with 2020 data, factoring in different trends such as change in eligible voters and demographics, to determine the projected number of undecided votes. Assuming a vote for Cori in 2018 will be a vote for Cori in 2020, I generate a priority list based on the highest number of votes that could be attained in different precincts. And while I could say more because I think it's cool, I'll spare you from the professional monotony, but to add to my previous point, this isn't the only time volunteers could've been mathematically optimized. There really is a great need for technology in the grassroots campaign space, and while I believe that I am making a difference, I am ultimately only one person.

For better or for worse, I am only one person.

\*\*\*

My August 4th begins so early that the Starbucks on Dale is not even open.

At the office, there are tables with computers followed by lines of volunteers being told which location to go to at the guidance of my algorithm, and I feel a slight sense of pride. Knowing I was able to produce meaningful work from what I learned at my school that gives me clinical depression made all the Saturday nights alone in the library and breaking down wondering if I would ever be enough, worth it.

A fellow colleague assigns me a location, which is a mid-sized Catholic church about twenty minutes away where there is quite literally no one there for the opponent. There are people advocating for mayor and other election positions, but not one single person here to advocate for everyone's favorite fifty-two-year political dynasty.

I guess that goes to show people's comfortability and resistance to change. Ignorance is bliss for those who can ignore, and why care when you can live south of Delmar and avoid seeing the manifestations of social issues that you avoid, perpetuate, and do nothing to solve?

It's easy. It's easy to think the world is a good place with a nice reality that isn't entirely exploitative, because accepting that the issues in this world are there brings a significant weight that is much easier to avoid. It's easy for the white suburban middle class to think the greatest threat to peace is premarital sex.

And once again, I digress. There is a campaign to win.

***

The polls have closed, and I am back at the office. There's a bit of socially distanced and masked partying going on to avoid the intense fear I know we all have. Only ten people are allowed in the office at once and people who volunteered today are welcomed outside to join the fun. There's music playing, mostly pop, but not the type of cheesy playlist that would debut at a high school dance. Everyone seems to be having a genuinely good time because even amid the overbearing political turmoil, this is perhaps the greatest opportunity for a good time in a very long time.

Cori is not in sight, which is totally understandable. Amid this waiting period, I hope she's proud of herself, and regardless of the results, she carried the weight of a sum of battles for an entire county, worked to defeat structural poverty, inspired hundreds of thousands, and all the while being one of the only people I would ever say is truly *good*. Wherever she is, whomever she is with, I hope she is able to appreciate herself for all that she is.

As more people gather outside the office, my coworkers and I move to the back of the building and form a circle with metal chairs to watch the results come in. There are no words, no sounds, until Adrastos taps the reset for the fifth time in a span of seven seconds, after which the first set of results come in.

Shit.

Huge lead on the opponent.

My eyes widen and my chest tightens, afraid this entire campaign was another false reality I had created, signifying that I am incapable of discerning fact from delusion.

"This was only the mail-in, which was projected to have a strong lean for the opponent since it was mostly older voters," Adrastos states as though he can sense my internal break down.

Less than a quarter of the votes are in, but the opponent's lead is considerably large. The lead shrinks as more votes come in, but it still persists, nonetheless. Not until slightly less than half the results are in does the opponent's lead become marginal.

I can't believe this is it. The night will end whether we are defeated by a fifty-two-year political dynasty with millions of dollars from corporate funding or we defeat it in spite of all odds. This is it. Most of us working on this campaign will probably never see each other again. This is the rising action and there is no falling action; it just ends.

I can't help but think about how many people I've gotten so close to, only for them to disappear from my life suddenly. And you never truly know when the last time you speak to someone will be. And all the nights you lay awake engraining it within yourself they were vital for your life to function were all a waste. At the end of the day, the only person you truly ever have is yourself.

I'm not entirely disappointed by who I am. I'm incredibly fucking awkward, as we've established at least one thousand times, but I will meet new people who will never see that side of me, and at the end of the day, I will only ever introduce my cumulative self with all of my best memories.

The people in front of me have a million of their own thoughts in their head just like me at this moment. I'm just a body in this space to them, and in part, they are just a body in this space to me, as I sit here, in this metal chair, watching the votes come in, trying to solve all of existentialism and find a sliver of meaning in a life that feels so pointless.

Adrastos jolts up from his seat.

"All the votes are in. She did it!"

The silence shifts from a depressing silence to a holy-shit silence, and it seems silly to think we ever had doubts. Cori has shown time and time again she will defy all odds.

We get up from our chairs and run inside, jumping up and down chanting: "Who won them votes? We won them votes! Who won them votes? We won them votes!"

Cori appears from behind a curtain in a way that feels too cinematic to be real. She's so happy yet so humble, and I couldn't be happier to witness Missouri's first Black congresswoman accept her victory.

I pull out my phone and take a video.

"#W" I caption the video and post it to social media, immortalizing this huge win for the county, the country, but mostly for the team celebrating in front of me.

*This is only the beginning*, I think to myself as I leave the office, never to exist in this time and space again, never to see the people whom I have lived my life with. This is only the beginning.

# CHAPTER 15

# CYCLICAL

---

It's been a few months since the campaign ended. Cori continues to make headline after headline for her outstanding performance in Congress. My life, on the contrary, is as internally chaotic as ever, and I wish to say that I am whole, but I am as broken as ever.

Online learning in the middle of a pandemic in an apartment that's miles from my school and catalytic to isolation. Poor mental health, which could still never be worse than childhood, but still worse than bad. Car accident. Concussion. Sweating through multiple shirts in the span of an hour with the temperature set to sixty degrees because my mental health is horrendous enough to overpower homeostasis. Crying after online classes because I don't like the way I look in one of thirty rectangular boxes on my computer screen. Endlessly seeking surface-level male validation because it's easier than developing meaningful connections with the risk of being betrayed.

I am cold as ice with the consistency of plexiglass; I can handle everything until one instance makes me completely shatter.

That said, I am only nineteen. The version I have come to know of myself is a transient acquaintance, and she will leave sooner than I think.

Perception has everything to do with the perceiver, and those around me are merely smudged reflections of myself. The young barista at the Starbucks on Dale is struggling with existentialism, and I am certain of this because she looks up at me from her side of the counter as though my words will be some sign from the universe, hands me my drink with a sensible keen awareness, and tells me to have a good day with an untraceable hopefulness. And I know this because I do the same. When I listen to the radio, when I hear my name in public, I listen to the following words to see if they are meant for me. At the gas station, I check the donut rack because the universe will show me donuts if I should contact Chad. The rack is always empty.

Chad actually has contacted me a few times: nothing notable or even worth remembering because my life is more peaceful without him in it, and I can appreciate I can love someone but not love my life with them in it.

The fall semester is almost over, and I am now operating at about 70 percent brain capacity, operating enough for me to know the constant ambulance stream past the apartment and to the hospital beside me is a morbid reality of the rising COVID cases. The siren wakes me up multiple times throughout the night, and it interrupts my online classes. The grim environment is unavoidable, no matter how much I pretend otherwise.

I still have chronic headaches and can feel parts of my brain are missing, but it's starting to come back to me. There's this guy whom I've been consistently talking to for almost two years and have only met in-person once. We are still advancing in two completely separate Midwestern worlds, yet close enough that collision is possible.

The Dichotomy is slightly closer now, living in a different Chicago suburb and finishing his first semester of Columbia University online. He's quite miserable, probably equal as I—not that it's a contest, merely an observation.

We are both living through the same reality at different times. I lived through my rude awakening to elitism and imposter syndrome last year, and he's living through it now. Smoke and mirrors. Shared consciousness. We are reflections of each other.

In this cold December, I find myself at the same place I was nine months ago. Time isn't linear, just perceived that way.

"Should I come visit?"

I am once again looking for an escape, an alternate reality to get me through the day.

"Yes, come whenever"

He's fond of me, and I'm not entirely sure why he enjoys my company as much as he does.

And as I've been locked alone in my apartment with no friends or light, I've realized how abysmal that truly is. So now I'm on my way to his new apartment in his new Chicago suburb. I stopped drinking coffee because of my concussion, but if I could, I would be sipping a twenty-four-ounce iced caramel cloud macchiato as I think.

The drive feels more exciting since everything in this world has become monotonous and lost all meaning, and maybe the fact I am able to see excitement in flat land, billboards, and concrete is once again a reflection of my imagination, but I think it's too optimistic to give myself credit for having that much creativity.

***

"You should write about anarcho-primitivism."

The Dichotomy walks out of his room with a slight smile on his face—his signature smile (the one between a :) and a :|). He got new hair, new glasses, yet he carries his old, calculated idiosyncrasies. He's five foot eleven, a good height, and I never noticed his height until I asked, just now.

I told him I was doing a profile on him for my nonfiction writing class, which wasn't a lie. He's aware he's a character in my world he is living in.

We stand feet apart from each other on the wooded floor in our high black socks. Nothing to say. Nothing to discuss. Just enjoying being three feet apart in silence, together. The Dichotomy locks his eyes on mine, raises his eyebrows, and purses his lips with a slight upward curl.

"Do you want a tour?"

And we walk into his bedroom. Classic nineteen-year-old men. Although in this context, I do not think it's a sexual pursuit. There's something about deep talks that are arguably more intimate and catalyzed by the bedroom setting.

***

The last one-on-one bedroom encounter I had with a man was a few weeks ago. I invited him over, looking for an evening adventure. I had been selective about who I met up with. Only went out for essentials and coffee. Always wore a mask. I didn't see many people regularly, and the truth is I will always have significantly more fans—people I talk to but am separated from by my lack of vulnerability and stone-cold façade—than friends, but he was an exception, a risk I was willing to take.

"So what do you think of the Midwest?"

He was from Silicon Valley. The Mecca of tech. The Mecca of start-ups. I've been twice with my mother, and I had a feeling there was much more than meets the tourist eye. I have, of course, formulated my own mundane opinions about the Midwest. The people are fake. Interactions are psuedo. Everyone masks their judgements with sharp smiles.

"Are we going to fuck or no?"

Damn. Straight to the point. No games. No sugar.

"Nope. I'm good." I smiled and turned red. I was very taken aback and trying to hide my disappointment at another failed attempt at trying to form a connection with someone.

"Yeah, it's late. I should go."

He opened the door and left. No goodbye. Not even a wave.

To each their own.

\*\*\*

"My bed is really comfortable, definitely better than whatever they have at your school."

"That's literally not possible."

I have to flex on the Dichotomy even though he goes to Columbia. I lie down on his bed—definitely not better than the multi-thousand-dollar mattresses that come as a gift to the gut-wrenching rite of passage to my school. He glances down at his watch and widens his eyes.

"Ah, I have a call right now."

He jolts up and dashes to his computer. Scrambling between tabs and opening up spreadsheets—nothing but concentration. He grabs his phone. He puts himself on speaker, almost like he wants me to hear.

"How are you feeling about the Cowboys? My line projects +5.7 with 0.3 variance."

Dense, misogynistic, and egocentric are three words that come to mind when I think of the people who participate in fantasy football—in that order. Yet here I am, watching the Dichotomy synthesize data and weight variables to create regression lines that predict the outcome of football games to ultimately win his fantasy football league. His father does the same. They are comparing variances over the phone to minimize the standard error as they make their selections, and I just watch in full jealously that someone could have so much fun analyzing spreadsheets.

He ends the call with his father. "Do you want to watch a video about drugs?" He says, completely unfazed and deadpan.

"Sure."

He hops back into the bed, and we lay together in a very nonsexual way. The exact same way as lovers, but in a completely different way because although we are so physically close, I am simply holding onto the one guy who has not let me down, which requires great strength given there have been so many. He has one hand on my shoulder with his arm around me and one hand on his phone that he brings to our lines of vision.

"Why are you so cold?" He grabs my hand and brings it in front of me like a mysterious object I need to see to believe.

"Raynaud's."

"What?"

"Raynaud's. It's this really fun condition where I essentially have an ideal temperature, and if I experience any sort of deviation, my arteries just stop supplying blood, and I turn purple."

"Very anti-pog." "Pog" is the Dichotomy's new favorite word from this postmodern era.

"Get better diction, please."

He grabs my purple hand and examines it again, despite the proximity to a pure absence of light.

"You're the only blue life that matters."

I laugh, and even in that brief release of tension, it feels like the weight I've accumulated from years of anxiety and depression have gone away.

And with that, we talk some more—a lot, actually. Lying in his bed, I wrap myself around him and move my fingers through his hair. We are not in love, and we never will be. There's comfort in knowing there is order in this increasingly chaotic world.

"The marginal utility of your visit is quite high."

"Yes, and since it isn't significantly decreasing per util, I suppose I must return."

"Eventually there will be a number of utils where there will likely be a significant decrease in marginal utility,"

We are still the same nerdy kids we were when we first spoke. We will change. We will grow. Nothing exists outside the present.

Youth is precious.

# ACKNOWLEDGMENTS

———

I was only eighteen when this story took place and nineteen while writing it. This is only the beginning, and I couldn't have done it without others' support and encouragement.

There are many people to thank—friends, family, the baristas at the Starbucks on Dale, generic men with the personality of chalk that inspired me to write this, and everyone around me who has contributed to my perspective on life, so if I have even so much as passed you by on a street corner, thank you!

Additionally, I would like to give a special thanks to those who put in extra effort to bring this book to fruition:

| | |
|---|---|
| Pamela Stevermer | Fraye Beyene |
| Sharon Mebus | Nolen Bowerman |
| Sydney Essler | Travis Phulnauth |
| Kaitlin Day | Sejal Rajamani |
| Elijah Marshall | Jackson Cox |
| Mary Murray | Pryce Adade-Yebesi |
| Eric Koester | Christian Snipes |
| Clara Hudson | Kelechi Achilefu |
| Matt Gallen | Rose-Marie Mebus |
| William Workman | Missy Iten |

Sheila Fox
Lindsay Holder
Mark Kleeman
Courtney Trenti

Deborah Taffa
Celeste Pepitone-Nahas
Cora Lewis
Edward McPherson

# APPENDIX

———

**AUTHOR'S NOTE**

"Generation Z and Mental Health" *The Annie E. Casey Foundation (blog).* Updated May 22, 2021. https://www.aecf.org/blog/generation-z-and-mental-health

Keren, Eli. "What Is The Best Age to Write a Novel?" *Curtis Brown Creative (blog).* June 20, 2016. https://www.curtisbrowncreative.co.uk/what-is-the-best-age-to-write-a-novel/

Miller, E. Ce. "13 Millennial Memoirs That Prove You're Never Too Young To Tell Your Story." *Bustle,* October 3, 2017. https://www.bustle.com/p/13-memoirs-by-millennials-that-prove-youre-never-too-young-to-tell-your-story-2445135

**CHAPTER 1**

Thoreau, Henry David. *Walden; or, Life in the woods.* Boston: Ticknor and Fields, 1854.

**CHAPTER 2**

Green, John. *The Fault in Our Stars.* New York: Dutton Books, 2012.

## CHAPTER 7

Householder, Leigh. "Patient USA: The Delmar Divide" *Syneos Health Communications (blog)*. November 20, 2017. https://blog.collegevine.com/colleges-with-the-richest-students/

Peck, Timothy. "Top 10 Colleges with the Richest Students" *CollegeVine (blog)*. April 8, 2020. https://blog.collegevine.com/colleges-with-the-richest-students/

Vaidya, Anuja. "Survey: 1 in 5 Americans can't afford necessary care" *MedCity News*, April 1 2021. https://medcitynews.com/2021/04/survey-1-in-5-americans-cant-afford-necessary-care/

## CHAPTER 8

Allen, Jonathan. "The real reason moderate Democrat Lacy Clay just lost his primary fight" NBC News, August 5 2020. https://www.nbcnews.com/politics/politics-news/real-reason-moderate-missouri-democrat-just-lost-his-primary-fight-n1235878

Ballotpedia. "Missouri's 1st Congressional Election, 2018." Accessed on October 11, 2021. https://ballotpedia.org/Missouri%27s_1st_Congressional_District_election,_2018

Ballotpedia. "United States Senate Election in Missouri, 2016." Accessed on October 11, 2021. https://ballotpedia.org/United_States_Senate_election_in_Missouri,_2016

Lears, Rachel, dir. *Knock Down the House*. Jubilee Films, Atlas Films, Artemis Rising. 2019. https://www.netflix.com/title/81080637

## CHAPTER 9

Close the Workhouse. *The Campaign*. 2020. https://www.closetheworkhouse.org/

Congresswoman Cori Bush. "Biography". Accessed July 16, 2021. https://bush.house.gov/about

## CHAPTER 11

Thoreau, Henry David. *Walden; or, Life in the woods.* Boston: Ticknor and Fields, 1854.